STEEL SERVES THE NATION

Chief Executive Officers of United States Steel Corporation

IRVING S. OLDS	ENDERS M. VOORHEES	BENJAMIN F. FAIRLESS
Chairman of the Board of Directors	*Chairman of the Finance Committee*	*President*

STEEL SERVES THE NATION

1901 - 1951

THE FIFTY YEAR STORY OF UNITED STATES STEEL

By DOUGLAS A. FISHER

Office of Assistant to Chairman,
United States Steel Corporation

UNITED STATES STEEL CORPORATION

COVER PHOTOGRAPH
*Blast furnaces at world's
largest integrated steel mill,
Gary Works, Gary, Indiana*

Inquiries for information regarding this book
should be addressed to J. Carlisle MacDonald,
Assistant to Chairman, United States Steel
Corporation, 71 Broadway, New York 6, N. Y.

Design by M. Peter Piening

Photographs of contemporary
U. S. Steel operations by Fritz Henle

Printed in the United States of America
by Lind Brothers

PICTURE CREDITS—Acme Newspictures, Inc.;
Admiral Corporation; "Adventures of Amer-
ica," by John A. Kouwenhoven, Harper &
Brothers; American Can Company; American
Car and Foundry Company; American Pe-
troleum Institute; Arabian-American Oil Com-
pany; Bettman Archive; Black Star; Bureau of
Reclamation; Camera Guild; Carnegie Corpo-
ration of New York; Cities Service Oil Com-
pany; Cooper Union; Fairchild Aerial Survey;
General Electric Company; Johnson and John-
son; Fred G. Korth; Martin Munkacsi; New
York Herald Tribune; Rockefeller Center;
Santa Fe Railroad; Scott-d'Arazien; Smith-
sonian Institution; Sun Valley; U. S. Air
Force; U. S. Army Signal Corps; U. S. Coast
Guard; U. S. Marine Corps; U. S. Navy; Wide
World Photos, Inc.

CONTENTS

PREFACE

United States Steel Corporation celebrates its Golden Anniversary this year with the satisfaction and pleasure that usually accompany the attainment of such a respectable age. Naturally we are proud and happy to have rounded out half a century in business with a record of successful achievement in our field of industrial activity. But the perilous international situation now existing restrains any tendency on our part to indulge in an elaborate birthday celebration.

It seems fitting, however, to observe our fiftieth birthday with the publication of a book summarizing United States Steel's outstanding achievements since its birth in 1901 and calling attention to their significance in terms of service to the nation. Furthermore, the appearance of "Steel Serves The Nation" may have timeliness and value as the United States prepares to defend itself against the present threat of Communist aggression.

Half a century is a short time in the history of a nation, but in the past fifty years scientific and industrial advances have completely transformed the everyday life of the average American. From the horse and buggy era we have progressed to a point where many products once considered inaccessible luxuries to most of our citizens are now regarded by them as ordinary necessities. This has been a monumental achievement in the development of our country. It was accomplished under a system of competitive free private enterprise, in which steel has played a major role as a basic metal.

The accomplishments and services recorded in this book are typical of those of American business in general during the present century. For that reason we hope that "Steel Serves The Nation" may help to make clear the virtues of our American way of business life—a way of life which may well be at stake in the emergency now facing this nation. Certainly the American people should strive to preserve an industrial system which in the past has functioned beneficially and successfully in their interest and, if unhindered, promises to continue to do so in the future. Such a system utilizes the energies and skills of our people most effectively for the defense of their freedom, and, when their liberties are no longer threatened, should enable them to resume the march of human progress in the United States.

The heart of the American way of life for business is the incentive and progress generated by competition among producers constantly endeavoring to improve their products, to reduce their operating costs, to enlarge their markets and to realize a fair return on their investments. Profit is the compelling motive in any risk-taking business enterprise. Profitable and successful industrial projects carry with them a rich overflow of benefits to the public in the form of better homes, better automobiles, better refrigerators, better television sets, better transportation facilities and thousands of other products of improved quality which often bear a lower price.

United States Steel commenced operations on April 1, 1901. Up to January 1, 1951, it had produced about 940 million tons of steel. In one form or another, that steel has been used by practically every industry in the land. United States Steel has helped substantially to build America and to make it the powerful nation it is today. Technology and research have enabled the development of new and improved steels capable of uses not possible fifty years ago. There has been a ceaseless effort on the part of United States Steel to improve efficiency and to secure a better product at every stage of its operations—from the mining of the iron ore and coal through the coke ovens, blast furnaces, Bessemer, open hearth and electric furnaces, on down to the rolling and finishing mills.

The principal achievements of United States Steel since 1901 are the subject of this book. Directly or indirectly they have benefited millions of Americans in their daily lives. We are proud of the fact that United States Steel has served this nation to the best of its ability both in war and in peace.

Now the thoughts and energies of United States Steel are directed toward increasing its capacity and production in order to do its part in supplying the vast quantity of steel presently needed for military and essential civilian requirements. Responding to the country's call for more steel, following the Communist invasion of South Korea, the Corporation last July embarked on a defense expansion program which will add 4,300,000 tons of annual ingot capacity by the end of 1952.

To provide steel for the needs of the country in the present emergency, the American steel industry is installing capacity more rapidly and is producing more steel than at any previous time in its history. On January 1, 1951, the annual steel capacity of American steel mills totaled 104 million tons, about equal to the combined capacity of the rest of the world. The American steel industry produced more than two million tons of steel in one week in January 1951 for the first time on record. At that rate, the United States could produce a greater tonnage of steel in twenty weeks than we have reason to believe the Soviet Union and its satellite nations produced in the entire year of 1950. Steel capacity in the United States is increasing month by month and projects now authorized by various steel companies will bring the total annual steelmaking capacity of this nation to 118 million tons by the end of 1952. And the industry has placed no limit upon its eventual size. Further expansion is likely to take place to keep pace with changing conditions in the future, as has been regularly true in the past.

This country's present steel capacity and the accelerated pace of expansion since war broke out in Korea last June should be heartening news to the American people. The steel industry of the United States is prepared to manufacture enough steel to provide our nation with the sinews of war for the eventual defeat of any enemy or group of enemies, while still producing sufficient steel for essential civilian needs.

As one of the oldest and largest companies in the industry, we should like to pay a highly deserved tribute to the other steel companies of the United States for their many notable advancements in steelmaking and for the unfailing dedication of their services to the best interests of the nation—facts which make us proud to be their competitor and fellow industry member. We should like also to make grateful acknowledgment to our thousands of customers for their helpful cooperation in mastering problems in the manufacture of steel products for their use and for the close and friendly associations which we have enjoyed with them over the years—a relationship which we earnestly hope may continue unchanged indefinitely into the future.

On behalf of the directors and officers of United States Steel, it is a privilege to express deep appreciation to the men and women of the Corporation, both the 300,000 men and women presently employed, and those no longer active in our operations, whose skill, diligence and loyalty over the years have enabled United States Steel to safeguard and enhance the interests of its stockholders and to achieve fifty years of successful service to the nation.

IRVING S. OLDS
Chairman, Board of Directors

July, 1951.

PART ONE

CHAPTER ONE

ORIGIN AND FORMATION

ORIGIN

In less than one hundred years, the everyday life of the American people has been changed more radically than for any other people during a similar period in world history. We passed quite literally from one form of civilization to another—from the Iron Age to the Steel Age.

In 1860 agriculture was our chief source of wealth production and we ranked second as a manufacturing nation. Our young industries were emerging from the handicraft and small shop stage to the first real factories. America was poised, so to speak,

to take off on a great industrial expansion which in thirty-four years enabled us to become the world's foremost industrial nation, producing goods in 1894 double the value of Great Britain's output.

To take that giant stride forward, one essential thing was needed—steel in mass production quantities at an economical price. Industry's most pressing need was an abundant supply of a metal as cheap as iron but stronger and more durable.

Bessemer process introduced the Steel Age in the 1860's. An artist's conception of early Bessemers in blow.

Agriculture absorbed most of our productive energies before we passed from the Iron Age to the Steel Age.

The chief use of Bessemer steel in the last century was to make rails for the rapidly expanding railroads.

STEEL AGE BEGINS WITH BESSEMER PROCESS

For centuries iron had been man's chief metal. It had served him well for most industrial purposes until the last half of the nineteenth century. But iron, generally speaking, lacks the strength, enduring qualities and versatility of steel. Iron simply could not stand up to all the requirements that were to be demanded of a basic metal in modern civilization. Iron rails, for instance, under comparatively light traffic, lasted only two years. Modern steel rails are good on main lines for an average of eighteen years, after which they serve for an indefinite period on side lines.

Steel, like iron, had been manufactured for centuries, but only in small amounts. It was rare and precious and was used mostly in sharp-cutting instruments and tools. In 1837, when Andrew Carnegie was born, steel cost 25 cents a pound, or $500 a ton. The scarcity and high price were due to the time and labor consumed in producing small quantities by the processes then used.

Who was going to find a way to produce steel, not by pounds, but by the thousands of tons which would be needed to build factories, railroads, bridges and the myriad other products of a bustling, thriving America, eager to march onward to industrial greatness? The answer was first supplied by an American, William Kelly, a native of Pittsburgh. It was he who first discovered a steelmaking process which was to make it possible for civilization to pass from the Iron Age to the Steel Age.

Kelly began experiments at his ironworks near Eddyville, Kentucky, in 1847 and steamboats with boilers made of his "refined iron" were plying the Ohio River several years before Henry Bessemer, in England, independently conceived of a steelmaking process similar in principle to Kelly's. But due in part to Kelly's poor business management and to the strange twists of fortune, the process became permanently identified with the name of Bessemer.

After a slow start, the output of Bessemer steel

14

in the United States went forward by leaps and bounds. In 1867, a total of 22,000 tons of steel was produced by various processes in this country, of which 3,000 tons were Bessemer steel. Within the space of thirteen years, demand for the new metal had boosted the annual production of Bessemer converters beyond the million-ton mark.

The Bessemer process had brought in the Steel Age with a rush, and manufacturers of all kinds were eagerly taking advantage of the increased supply of the metal. Industrial America was on the march.

OPEN HEARTH FURNACE INTRODUCED

In the 1870's another revolutionary steelmaking process was introduced in America—the open hearth furnace, which poured out additional tonnages of steel for our thriving industries, attaining an annual output of more than 100,000 tons in ten years.

The American steel industry was now ready, with its Bessemer converters and open hearth furnaces, to challenge the supremacy of Great Britain as the world's foremost steel producer. In 1889 we forged to the front and have ever since remained the world's leading producer of steel.

More vividly than words, however, figures portray the story of America's spectacular growth from 1867, when the Bessemer process was well launched, to the end of the century. In those thirty-three years, steel production increased from roughly 22,000 tons to 11,400,000 tons, or more than 500 times. Population of the United States more than doubled—from 37,000,000 to 76,000,000. The 39,000 miles of railroads spread out into a nation-wide network of 259,000 miles, stimulating the growth of towns and cities and opening up markets for the products of the factory and the farm.

The amount of steel produced per person in a nation is one of the keys to its degree of industrialization and living standards. Here, the growth in thirty-three years is striking. When the Steel Age began, 1.2 pounds of steel were produced per person in the United States. By 1900 the figure had risen to 300 pounds per person. This meant that year after year more steel was going into the erection of factories and their machines, into trains, ships, buildings, agricultural implements, telephone and telegraph systems, "tin" cans, sewing machines, typewriters, printing presses and hosts of other products which were improving the living standards in America on a rapidly-rising scale.

William Kelly, first inventor of the new steelmaking process. Center picture, one of his early converters.

Henry Bessemer, after whom the process was named. His experiments were begun seven years after Kelly's.

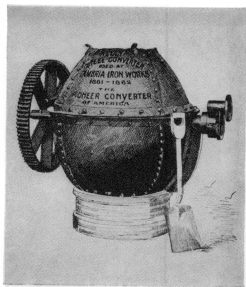

Charles M. Schwab, who played a prominent role in formation of U. S. Steel and was its first president.

MASS MARKETS REQUIRE MASS PRODUCTION

In the closing years of the nineteenth century profound changes were taking place in the nation. We were like a youth outgrowing a boy's clothes. Our economy was enlarging at such a rate that some industries were seeking more efficient means of production through integrated operations. Large scale production was new on the American scene. It took a wrench in thinking for some people to realize the magnitude of America, and that mass markets require mass production.

Two Americans stand out in the late 1890's as men with sufficient vision to foresee that America's future industrial needs could best be served by a more complete integration of steelmaking operations. They were Elbert H. Gary, popularly known as Judge Gary, and Charles M. Schwab. Judge Gary was then president of the Federal Steel Company, the largest

Andrew Carnegie, the sale of whose company made possible the founding of United States Steel in 1901.

western steel concern. Charles Schwab was directing affairs of Andrew Carnegie's company, then the premier steel producer in the world. The two men were business competitors but circumstances were to bring them together to fulfill a common dream.

CARNEGIE WISHES TO RETIRE

The chain of events which ultimately brought the two men together was precipitated by the desire of Andrew Carnegie to sell his steel company. He had become a very wealthy man, and around 1900 it became generally known that he wanted to retire and fulfill an often-expressed wish to go down in history not as America's greatest steel master but as its greatest philanthropist.

Andrew Carnegie, who more than any one person made Pittsburgh famous as a great steel city, was the son of poor Scottish immigrants. His first job was as a bobbin-boy in a cotton mill for wages of $1.20 a

week, and his next was as a telegraph messenger. From these humble beginnings he became the builder of a virtual empire of steel in his own company. In 1900 it was reorganized as the Carnegie Company. As president he installed a man whom he had brought up through the ranks, Charles M. Schwab.

REMARKABLE CAREER OF CHARLES M. SCHWAB

Schwab's life has often been cited as an inspirational success story. He had the rare distinction of being the only man in history to play a leading role in founding and then becoming president of the world's two largest steel companies—United States Steel Corporation and Bethlehem Steel Company.

As a chubby-faced, whistling boy he used to drive his father's stagecoach over the mountains from his native Loretto, Pennsylvania, to the nearby town of Cresson, which then happened to be the summer

Left, below, Pittsburgh in 1901. Andrew Carnegie more than any person made it a famous steel center.

Isabella Furnaces, among the most famous Pittsburgh blast furnaces in final quarter of the 19th century.

residence of Andrew Carnegie. The barefoot boy more than once held the famous man's horses, little dreaming that he would later become one of his partners and generalissimo of the Carnegie interests.

To better his fortune Charlie moved down country and at the age of seventeen entered the steel industry as a stake driver for one dollar a day at Carnegie's Edgar Thomson Works. Once his exceptional abilities came to the notice of the Scotsman, his rise was meteoric. At twenty-five he was superintendent of the Homestead Works and by his thirty-fifth year he was president of the Carnegie Company.

Schwab was keenly alert to the need of integration in the steel industry and was introducing it in some of the Carnegie mills. As a production man, no one realized better than he that the economical production of steel on a large scale called for the entire chain of operations under one management, from collecting and transporting the raw materials to loading finished steel into railroad cars for shipment to customers. Schwab was also a strong opponent of "trusts." "No one," he once said, "has a clearer appreciation than myself of the evil that lurked in the trust scheme . . . its fundamental principles were the restriction of trade, the increase of prices and the throttling of competition . . . a trinity that would wreck any proposition, business, political or social."

GARY THE SQUARE DEALER

In Chicago, another man, Judge Gary, was also dreaming of integrated steel operations which, in his words, "would permit not only the more economical production of steel for American consumption, but would also make possible competition on favorable terms in foreign markets," thus providing additional

---

Judge Elbert H. Gary, principal founder of United States Steel and its chief executive officer for 26 years.

outlets for steel production. Equally with Schwab, Judge Gary abhorred the evils of "trusts," and believed that the organization he had in mind, instead of restricting trade, would tend "to sustain trade and foster competition."

Such a business attitude was inherent in Judge Gary's nature, molded by the strict principles of his parents, who were descended from a long line of deeply religious, honest, thrifty and hard-working pioneers. Judge Gary was born on a farm near Warrenville, Illinois, on October 8, 1846. At the age of eighteen he chose the legal profession as his career and was graduated from the Union College of Law in Chicago at the head of his class. He began the practice of law in Chicago and rapidly became known as an able lawyer, with a passion for fair and just dealing. His title of "Judge" remained with him after he served two terms as Judge of Du Page County, Illinois. Within twenty years after he was admitted to the bar, Judge Gary stood at the front rank of his profession in Chicago.

GARY ENTERS THE STEEL BUSINESS

In 1898, the Illinois Steel Company, then the largest western steel producer, asked Judge Gary's advice on the purchase of a railroad running from Chicago to its plant at Joliet, Illinois. He suggested that what the company needed to meet competition was not so much a short-line railroad but rather what he termed a "rounded proposition," embracing the whole range of steelmaking operations.

Judge Gary's advice was followed. With the Illinois Steel Company as a nucleus and with the financial backing of J. Pierpont Morgan, Judge Gary undertook negotiations which led to the formation of the Federal Steel Company. Judge Gary was appointed president of the new company, with headquarters in New York.

FORMATION

CARNEGIE'S FIRST OVERTURES

The stage was now set with the principal characters who were to take part in a series of events culminating in the formation of United States Steel Corporation. In sounding out possible purchasers of his company, Carnegie's first overture was to the Standard Oil Company, but this resulted in failure. After the formation of the Federal Steel Company in 1898, he felt that here was a possible buyer. He turned to his chief partner at that time, Henry C. Frick—a man of extraordinary business ability who had begun as a poor boy and with his own hands had built up the enormously successful H. C. Frick Coke Company of western Pennsylvania. When he joined Carnegie as a partner, Frick had brought his properties with him into the Carnegie Company.

In the spring of 1899, Carnegie dispatched Frick as an emissary to Judge Gary to propose a merger of the two steel concerns. As the talks progressed, the two men could not come to a meeting of minds and the matter was dropped.

PRESSURE BY CARNEGIE

The canny Scotsman, Carnegie, meanwhile, was not idle. He let it be known that he was planning to build a $12,000,000 tube plant, covering 5,000 acres at Conneaut, Ohio. This was aimed at the National Tube Company in which Morgan was interested. Also in Carnegie's announced plans was the construction of a railroad to transport his steel from Pittsburgh to the seacoast. This was a direct thrust at the Pennsylvania Railroad in which Morgan was also financially interested. Finally, to fight the American Steel & Wire Company, Carnegie allowed the word to pass along that he would erect a giant wire-making plant near Pittsburgh. On hearing this news the steel industry was thrown into an uproar.

Meanwhile, Carnegie and Frick quarreled violently and severed their partnership. In the spring of 1900 the Carnegie interests were reorganized into a new company, the Carnegie Company, as previously mentioned, with Charles M. Schwab as president.

Shortly after he assumed his new duties, Schwab appeared at the Federal Steel Company's office one day and suggested to Judge Gary that he buy the Carnegie properties. The Federal Company was not attaining the "rounded proposition" which Judge Gary had originally anticipated. To complete his plans, particularly to establish foreign outlets for steel, Gary wanted more money but Morgan could not be convinced of its necessity. Gary needed no persuasion to take Schwab's proposition to Morgan. But still the banker was obdurate. "I would not think of it," he told Gary. "I don't believe I could raise the money."

THE FAMOUS DINNER OF 1900

Morgan was still obdurate in December of 1900 when he attended in New York a dinner famous in the annals of the steel industry. It was a testimonial dinner tendered to Schwab by Edward Simmons and Charles Stuart Smith, New York financiers. Schwab gave the principal talk.

As Burton J. Hendrick described it in his book, "The Life of Andrew Carnegie," Schwab "took the assembled bankers up to the mountain top and spread before their startled eyes the splendor of his universe of steel. The unfolded prospect was a new and dazzling one." Instead of having one mill produce ten, twenty or fifty different products, he pointed out, the greatest economies could be realized by having one mill limit itself to a single "line" such as rails, or beams or plates and make that one product continuously. He told of the savings that could be effected in transportation alone, which then constituted one-third of the price of steel. Reminding his listeners that most of the plants had been located in a haphazard fashion during the infancy of the industry, he argued that a more judicious selection of sites in relation to markets and transportation lines would enhance efficiency. Throughout, he emphasized that the economies which he described would permit steel to be sold at lower prices.

To accomplish the ends he had in view, Schwab went on, no existing concern was large enough. Only a corporation larger than any then existing, he said, encompassing ore fields, transportation facilities, all kinds of mills and finishing plants, could achieve the degree of integration which would place the steel industry on a really scientific basis. But the type of amalgamation which had recently become familiar would not do, he declared. The practice of acquiring a monopoly, restricting output and raising prices, he condemned as little less than an industrial crime.

Schwab's speech made a profound impression on Morgan. After the dinner he drew Schwab aside and talked to him earnestly for half an hour. Several days later Morgan asked John W. Gates, who had organized the American Steel & Wire Company, to arrange a meeting with Schwab to discuss the matter further. One of Morgan's impelling motives in considering the purchase of the Carnegie interests was a desire to bring about stability in the steel industry by supporting the kind of combination which Schwab had painted in such glowing terms.

MORGAN IS CONVINCED

At this famous meeting, held in the library of Morgan's New York home, Robert Bacon, Morgan's partner, was present in addition to Schwab and Gates. The meeting began at 9 o'clock in the evening. Schwab did most of the talking. If he had revealed

Henry Clay Frick, partner of Carnegie and one of his first emissaries for the sale of his properties.

J. Pierpont Morgan with his son. Morgan, Sr., financed the purchase of companies forming U. S. Steel.

himself as a master salesman at the dinner a few evenings previous, he now displayed his vast and intimate knowledge as a steel production man. He set forth in encyclopedic thoroughness all the information he had gathered about steel in the preceding twenty years. At dawn, Morgan finally said, "Well, if Andy wants to sell, I'll buy. Go and find his price."

Carnegie, on receiving this news from Schwab, hesitated at first. Reason told him to accept, now that the chance to sell had come, but his emotional attachment to his company was strong. Finally he took a sheet of paper and with a lead pencil jotted down a figure—$400,000,000—and directed Schwab to take the paper to the banker.

UNITED STATES STEEL IS FORMED

Morgan accepted the terms and directed Judge Gary to draw up a plan of organization. The plan was approved by the banker and Judge Gary was then asked to put it into execution. After weeks of the most arduous work, Judge Gary, who, in the words of Robert Bacon, "directed it all," put together the United States Steel Corporation. It was incorporated on February 25, 1901, and was ready for business on April 1, with an authorized capitalization of $1,400,000,000.

The original member companies were: Carnegie Company, Federal Steel Company, American Steel & Wire Company, National Tube Company, National Steel Company, American Tin Plate Company, American Steel Hoop Company and American Sheet Steel Company. Shortly afterwards, the American Bridge Company and the Lake Superior Consolidated Iron Mines were acquired.

Charles M. Schwab was the first president of United States Steel and served until 1903 when he resigned. A few years later he became interested in the Bethlehem Steel Company, which he built up into the second largest steel producer in the country.

Judge Gary served for two years as Chairman of the Executive Committee and then became Chairman of the Board of Directors, a position he held until his death on August 15, 1927. If there is any one man who might be credited with the creation of United States Steel, that man is Elbert H. Gary. During the twenty-six years in which he served as its chief executive officer, he infused the Corporation with his spirit and personality and molded its policies and actions to accord with his own high ethical standards, which became widely known as the "Gary principles." The policies he established have remained substantially in effect to this day. As much as any business leader in the first quarter of this century he brought about a change of concept in the conduct of business. Judge Gary repeatedly said from the beginning that his objective was not to secure monopoly, but to sustain trade and foster competition. The effectiveness of this policy was evidenced in the months immediately following the formation of United States Steel, when the demand for steel was great but prices were 30 to 70 per cent lower than they were a year and a half before the Corporation was formed.

Judge Gary firmly believed in the public responsibility of large corporations. He was at the forefront of American industrialists in instituting welfare and safety programs and other measures for the betterment of working conditions. Perhaps the best estimate of Judge Gary's position in the steel industry and in American industry in general was given by Charles M. Schwab at a dinner in Judge Gary's honor in 1909. Schwab said in part: "The broad principles which you brought into this business were new to all of us who had been trained in a somewhat different school. Their effect was marvelous—their success unquestioned. It was a renaissance and a newness of things in this business that were necessary and invigorating."

THE GARY PRINCIPLES

I believe that when a thing is right, it will ultimately and permanently succeed.

The highest rewards come from honest and proper practice. Bad results come in the long run from selfish, unfair and dishonest conduct.

I believe in competition . . . that the race should be won by the swiftest, and that success should come to him who is most earnest and active and persevering.

I believe that no industry can permanently succeed that does not treat its employees equitably and humanely.

I believe thoroughly in publicity . . . The surest and wisest of all regulation is public opinion.

If we succeed as businessmen we must do it on principles that are honest, fair, lawful and just.

We must put and keep ourselves on a platform so fair, so high, so reasonable, that we will attract the attention and invite and secure the approval of all who know what we are doing.

We do not advocate combinations or agreements in restraint of trade, nor action of any kind which is opposed to the laws or to the public welfare.

We must never forget that our rights and interests are and should be subservient to the public welfare; that the rights and interests of the individual must always give way to those of the public.

CHAPTER TWO

GROWING WITH AMERICA

Great as was the expansion of our economy in the second half of the nineteenth century, it merely prepared us for another fifty years' growth surpassing anything ever accomplished by the mind and hand of man. In a country rich in natural resources, where basic freedoms favored the full development of man's capabilities, the American people developed an economic machine which now produces nearly one-half of all the goods manufactured in the entire world.

America's share of manufactured products is only one index of our economic expansion and of our progress in many fields. We enjoy numerous goods and services which are unattainable luxuries for most people in other nations. Four out of five automobiles on this earth are running on the highways and byways of the U. S. A. Americans own nearly six out of ten of the world's telephones and more than half of all existing radio sets. Science's latest wonder,

U. S. Steel has grown with America, building new capacity to help meet the increased steel needs of the nation.

television, is in twelve million American homes.

OTHER PRICELESS BENEFITS

In this half century, other benefits have been bestowed upon us. The average American wage earner has almost twenty more hours of leisure a week in which to enjoy a greatly improved standard of living, considerably higher than that of any other wage earner in the world. Around 1900, in order to buy a dozen eggs, the average manufacturing employee had to work 78 minutes. In 1950, it took him only 28 minutes, in spite of the fact that food prices have risen far more than other necessities since the end of World War II.

A better family table, increased knowledge of diet and hygiene, great advancements in medicine and labor-saving appliances in the home—all have contributed to improved health and longer life in the nation. The average American born in 1900 could expect to live about 49 years. Born in 1950, he could look forward to a life of about 68 years—an actual gain of 19 years. In less than half a century the average life expectancy in America has increased almost 39 per cent!

BIGNESS AND VISION

The creation of wealth and jobs on a steadily rising scale, except for some interruptions, has characterized the phenomenal progress of the United States in the present half century. Since 1900, twenty new major industries have come into being—automotive, aviation, radio, rayon, nylon, plastics, frozen foods and television, to name a few—which have boosted our total national income and provided millions of jobs. The automotive industry alone employs nearly 9,000,000 men and women in the making, selling, driving and servicing of motor vehicles.

THE ROLE OF RESEARCH

Two features of our economic growth in this century stand out conspicuously. One is large-scale research and the other is large-scale production. The pre-eminent position of the United States as a manufacturing nation is based first of all on the products of the research laboratory. Many of the modern miracles which we take for granted as the air we breathe were possible only because large companies could afford to spend the immense sums required for their research and development. Eleven weary years and $27,000,000 were spent in research before one pound of nylon was sold. U. S. Steel devoted over fifteen years to developing the electrolytic process for tin plating which was perfected in the nick of time to prevent a critical shortage of canned food for the home front in World War II. To provide us with new and improved products, all of which create wealth and furnish jobs, "big business" spends around half a billion dollars a year on research.

LARGE-SCALE PRODUCTION

The second important factor in America's economic growth has been the development of large industries. To supply mass markets in this vast nation, whose population and living standards increase year after year, requires transportation, manufacturing and distribution on a mammoth scale never before undertaken in the history of the world.

Just as it took vision and courage for our early pioneers to blaze trails into the unknown, so it has called for men of vision to plan for large-scale, low-cost production, as we march ahead into new frontiers in this age of science and the machine.

BIG AND LITTLE BUSINESS GROW TOGETHER

The growth of large mass production industries has multiplied the number of small businesses. The automobile industry spends half of its income in buying materials, parts and services from 25,000 small enterprises. Another large manufacturer buys from 31,000 small businesses and sells through 200,000 small concerns. U. S. Steel spends nearly 40 per cent of its receipts from sales in buying goods and services from 54,000 suppliers, 92 per cent of which are small businesses. Or, seen from another standpoint, eight out of every ten customers to whom U. S. Steel sells its products are small companies.

HALF A CENTURY OF STEEL EXPANSION

The basic metal for the growth in our American economy during the present century has been steel. Without mass quantities of steel at economical prices,

Working model of a new steel mill. U. S. Steel has expanded its steelmaking capacity threefold since 1901.

no nation can rise to industrial greatness.

The steel industry of the United States has increased its productive capacity at a considerably faster rate than the growth of our population. Since the beginning of the century, the population has a little more than doubled, while the steel industry's capacity has been multiplied more than four times and its annual production has been multiplied more than eight times. At the beginning of the present century, the steel industry produced 300 pounds of steel per person. In 1950 it produced 1,276 pounds for every man, woman and child in America.

U. S. Steel has endeavored to enlarge its capacity and production from time to time to help meet the increasing steel needs of a growing nation. The Corporation's annual capacity has increased from 10,600,000 tons in 1901 to 33,900,000 tons at the start of 1951—roughly three times as much. Other American steel companies, in the same period of years, expanded their annual capacity from 13,500,-000 to 70,400,000 tons—or to roughly five times as much. In other words, whereas U. S. Steel possessed

about 44 per cent of the total annual steel producing capacity of the United States in 1901, reaching a high of 52 per cent in 1907, today U. S. Steel's proportion of the total national steel capacity is slightly less than one-third and that of competitors is a trifle more than two-thirds.

From a production standpoint, the trend has been even more pronounced. As other existing steel companies grew larger and new ones were formed, U. S. Steel's proportion of total American steel production declined more or less steadily from 66 per cent in 1901 to about 33 per cent in the early 1930's, where it has remained virtually unchanged.

STEEL EXPANSION IN RECENT TIMES 1940 TO JUNE 1950

Expansion of the steel industry's capacity in recent times may be divided into two periods. The first includes World War II and the postwar years up to the outbreak of the war in Korea in June 1950. The second covers the defense expansion program begun in mid-1950 and now projected to December 31, 1952.

To meet the swollen demands for steel during World War II and the years immediately following, the American steel industry accomplished an expansion program surpassed in magnitude only by the present defense plans. In slightly more than one decade—from 1940 to mid-1950—the steel industry added 19,000,000 tons of annual capacity, bringing the total annual capacity to more than 100,000,000 tons for the first time in history. Close to half of this ten-year expansion in the steel industry was completed after the close of World War II in an effort to catch up with the clamorous demands of the public for new homes, automobiles, home appliances and other products requiring steel which had accumulated during the conflict when little steel was available for such purposes. The already high demand for consumer goods, other than automobiles, was pushed still higher by the abnormally high marriage rate, which reached a peak of 2,300,000 in 1946.

The problems of the steel industry in meeting this tidal wave of demands were made all the more difficult for two reasons. The nation suffered a serious production loss of 29,000,000 tons of steel from the end of the war to June 30, 1950, due to strikes and work stoppages. After processing, this production loss would have been enough steel to make nearly 180,500,000 average size electric refrigerators, or more than 11,600,000 average passenger automobiles, or more than 5,800,000 six-room houses, utilizing the maximum amount of steel in the dwellings. Then, too, considerable tonnages of steel had to be diverted from consumer industries for the construction of the new steel-producing facilities which were needed.

In view of these factors, the amazing fact about postwar steel shortages is that they were not any worse. The appetite of a man at his first meal after breaking a fast is no measure of his normal needs. If he were offered as a regular diet the quantity of food he asked for when half starved, he would complain that he was being overfed.

DEFENSE EXPANSION PROGRAM JUNE 1950 TO DECEMBER 31, 1952

When the United States attained the capacity to produce in excess of 100,000,000 tons of steel a year, it is possible that this would have been sufficient in normal circumstances to overcome accumulated steel shortages within a reasonable length of time. If not, it is certain that the steel industry would not have relaxed its expansion program until it could amply meet the steel needs of a growing population and an expanding economy. That has been the history of the American steel industry.

However, normal circumstances did not continue. Overnight the situation changed with the invasion of South Korea in June 1950, and the pressure for steel soon became even greater than before. Although the Korean war and the tense international situation caused the United States Government substantially to enlarge and speed up its defense program, this did not result in any appreciable increase in Government orders for steel deliveries during the last half of 1950. The immediate effect of the Korean war on the steel industry was to bring a flood of demands from civil-

A huge backlog of demand accumulated during World War II for new housing, automobiles, home appliances and other products requiring steel. To meet the need, the steel industry achieved record-breaking expansion.

ian buyers who apparently wanted to lay in a supply of steel products and of various articles made of steel before the anticipated purchases of the Government would compel the institution of priorities and allocations. By July, however, it was already plainly evident that the military and defense needs of the Government would require greatly increased steel capac-

more rapidly and producing more steel than at any previous time. In January 1951, the industry produced more than 2,000,000 tons of steel in one week for the first time on record. At that rate, the United States could produce in about twenty weeks as much steel as it is estimated the Soviet Union and its satellite nations turned out in the entire year 1950.

ity. As a consequence, U. S. Steel and other steel companies energetically began on their own separate initiative a defense expansion program designed to bring the total annual capacity of this nation to 105,750,000 tons by the end of 1952. By January 1, 1951, the capacity had already reached 104,000,000 tons and shortly afterwards the capacity to be in operation on December 31, 1952, was boosted to 118,000,000 tons annually. It is likely that additional projects of different steel companies will raise the total figure even higher.

The American steel industry is building capacity

The American steel industry can now produce sufficient steel to supply armaments for victory over any potential enemy or group of enemies, while still taking care of our essential civilian needs. Another 14,000,000 tons of capacity are to be added within two years. This means that the 118,000,000

Greater steel production requires more iron ore—one of U. S. Steel's new large ore vessels under construction.

For defense and civilian purposes, the steel industry is pouring more steel from its furnaces than ever before.

tons yearly capacity of the industry by the end of 1952 will enable it to produce millions of tons more steel than the estimated total quantity made by all the rest of the world combined in 1950, and 28,000,000 tons above the American production in the peak year of World War II.

No person can predict with any degree of certainty the future steel requirements for our civilian and defense needs. The steel industry of the United States has placed no limit to its eventual size, and it can be relied upon to provide the needed tonnage for the Government's defense and military programs, however large they prove to be, and for essential needs of the home economy.

FAIRLESS WORKS

Artist's conception of U. S. Steel's East Coast Mill on the Delaware River near Morrisville, Pennsylvania, to be completed by the end of 1952. *Story on page 34.*

LEGEND: 1. Ore Storage Yard · 2. Blast Furnaces · 3. Coal Storage · 4. Coke Ovens · 5. Coal Chemicals Plant · 6. Open Hearth Plant · 7. Soaking Pits · 8. Slab—Blooming Mill · 9. Billet Mill · 10. Bar Mill 11. Hot Strip Mill · 12. Sheet and Tin Finishing Mill · 13. Maintenance Shops · 14. Industrial Relations Building · 15. General Office · 16. Laboratory · 17. Power House · 18. National Tube Company Plant

U. S. STEEL'S PART IN THE EXPANSION PROGRAM

Following the close of World War II, U. S. Steel began to enlarge and improve its facilities in an effort to help meet the nation's pressing need for steel. In a five-year period, beginning January 1, 1946, it increased capacity by 5,000,000 tons, or roughly 17.5 per cent. This brought the Corporation's annual steel capacity to 33,900,000 tons on January 1, 1951.

After the invasion of South Korea, U. S. Steel undertook to determine how it could most expeditiously further expand its steelmaking capacity. The first step in the program was completed in the last half of 1950, when 1,800,000 tons of capacity were added. Authorizations were later made for 2,500,000 tons of additional steel capacity, making a total of 4,300,000 tons in U. S. Steel's defense expansion program to be completed by the end of 1952.

THE FAIRLESS WORKS

The largest project in U. S. Steel's current program is construction of a wholly integrated Atlantic seaboard mill of 1,800,000 ingot tons capacity, to be

Benjamin F. Fairless, U. S. Steel President, at the ground-breaking ceremonies of the new Fairless Works.

called Fairless Works, in honor of Benjamin F. Fairless, President of U. S. Steel. Ground was broken for the new mill on March 1, 1951, and completion is scheduled by the end of 1952. Fairless Works will be located at tidewater on the Delaware River near Morrisville, Pennsylvania, across the river from Trenton, New Jersey. The site is approximately 20 miles from Philadelphia. The logical area for distribution of the mill's products is in the Middle Atlantic and New England districts. Shipments can also be made by water directly to foreign ports.

It is expected that part of the iron ore for the furnaces of Fairless Works will come from the rich deposits discovered by U. S. Steel in Venezuela in 1947, described more fully in Chapter Seven. Pending the availability of Venezuelan ore, the new plant will use other foreign as well as domestic ores.

ECONOMICAL STEEL PRICES

Steel, the basic metal, is supplied at an economical price. The average price of all finished steel products is a little under five cents a pound. Some steel products sell for less than three and a half cents a pound. There is practically nothing that a housewife can buy in a grocery store for as little as three and a half cents a pound—sugar, flour, potatoes, or the commonest variety of vegetables. Steel undersells every metal in the world. It is cheaper than the cheapest material from which clothing is made, cheaper than any of the fibers that go into that material. It is cheaper than the lumber that goes into homes, cheaper than the pulp upon which the daily newspaper is printed. Steel is actually cheaper than soil procured from the city florist for potting plants in your home!

These price comparisons take on an added significance when one considers the high capital investment in the steel industry and the wide range of operations involved in producing a ton of steel.

The incredibly low selling price of steel is due to several factors. One is the lively competition existing within the steel industry and between steel and products such as aluminum, wood, plastics, cement, slate, tiles, and others. Another factor is the constantly improved efficiency in steelmaking operations, from raw materials through the furnaces, rolling mills and finishing operations.

U. S. STEEL'S PRICE POLICY

U. S. Steel's price policy was stated in the first report to stockholders in 1902: "The demand for the products of the several companies has been so great that prices could easily have been advanced. Indeed, higher prices have been voluntarily offered by consumers who were anxious for immediate execution of orders, but the companies have firmly maintained the position of not advancing prices, believing that the existing prices were sufficient to yield a fair return on capital and maintain the properties in satisfactory physical condition, and that the many collateral advantages to be gained in the long run by refusing to advance prices would be of substantial and lasting value, not only to the companies, but also to the general business interest of the country."

In general, steel prices are determined by competition. U. S. Steel has consistently followed the policy of selling its products at competitive prices. Its objective is to realize a profit at all times on all products, and it is guided by the long range philosophy that the lower the price of steel the more the needs of the public will be satisfied and the demand for steel stimulated.

In applying this policy, U. S. Steel has made only moderate price increases through the years, in spite of higher operating costs. This is strikingly illustrated in the accompanying chart. There it may be seen that from 1901 through 1950, hourly earnings of employees increased 809 per cent, the cost of new plants and equipment mounted 565 per cent, while iron and steel prices went up 192 per cent.

PROFITS AND SHAREHOLDERS

U. S. Steel, like every other corporate enterprise in our free, competitive system, exists to serve its

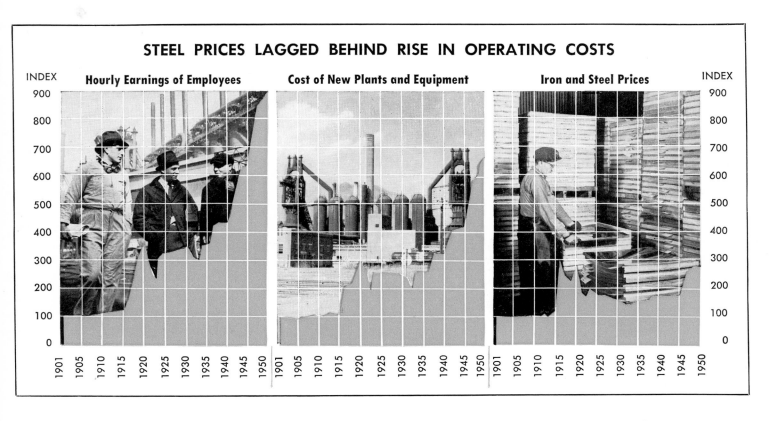

STEEL PRICES LAGGED BEHIND RISE IN OPERATING COSTS

customers and ultimately the public, and at the same time to make enough profit to pay a reasonable return to stockholders, while leaving sufficient funds to carry on the business.

The 260,000 stockholders of U. S. Steel include men and women from all walks of life in every state of the nation. Shares are also owned by insurance companies, industrial and other companies, trustees, charitable, educational, medical, religious and other organizations. No individual owns as much as three-tenths of one per cent of either the outstanding common or preferred stock.

These persons and institutions are the exclusive owners of U. S. Steel. They are the only individuals and groups who receive part of the profits in dividends for the money they have invested in shares. The remaining part of the profits is reinvested in the business. There are no other profits, "concealed," "undistributed," or otherwise.

No aspect of our competitive private enterprise system has been so much misrepresented and distorted as the subject of profits. In some quarters today, profits are without honor in a nation where they were the main incentive that brought us from a land of primitive wilderness to the richest, most powerful country on the face of the earth in the space of a few hundred years. Take away the incentive for profits and our progressive improvement in living standards would stop in its tracks.

In the past twenty years U. S. Steel's profits have been somewhat less than the average of forty-five other manufacturing industries. Those twenty years covered a depression and a war, when conditions were highly abnormal, but conditions are seldom normal for any length of time in the steel industry,

U. S. Steel's shareholders are in every part of the nation. More than half of the individual owners are women.

which is subject to wide fluctuations. During the period in question, there were seven years in which the holders of common stock received no dividends. U. S. Steel's profits from 1931 to 1950, inclusive, averaged 2.19 per cent of sales.

INCOME REINVESTED IN THE BUSINESS

As mentioned earlier, profits are used exclusively to pay dividends and to reinvest in the business. The latter sum is spent for new productive power— plants and tools—all of which mean new job opportunities. The amount that American industry is able to use for this purpose is of crucial importance, if our economy is to continue to expand and provide jobs for the growing population. On the amount that is annually reinvested in the business depend more and better jobs, more and better products, and more power and security in case of war.

There can hardly be a more dangerous attack on our private enterprise system than to question its right to reinvest in the business a portion of its income. To take away the means by which a company maintains, modernizes and expands its operations is similar to striking with an axe at the base of a tree. During the past twenty years, U. S. Steel's income reinvested in the business has averaged less than one cent of every sales dollar.

THE INDUSTRIAL FAMILY GROWS UP

Since its formation, U. S. Steel has enlarged and diversified its activities to meet the changing demands for steel as the economy of the nation has expanded. When the Corporation began to do business the horse-and-buggy era was on its way out.

In the intervening years, many new industries came into being, bringing with them new require-

ments for steel. Numerous old industries vanished, abolishing markets for certain forms of steel. When the hand-wound phonograph was in vogue, for example, it was sold by the millions. This created a large demand for the steel springs which made the phonograph run, and wire manufacturers hurriedly converted their equipment to supply this special market. For a number of years it was large and profitable. Then it disappeared with the advent of the electrically-operated phonograph. This typifies the many drastic changes in the demand for various steel products.

Markets for steel shifted also on a regional basis, as populations moved westward and to the Southwest and as the economy of various areas was developed. The discovery of petroleum in the West and Southwest is a case in point. Development of the petroleum industry vitally affected those regions and opened up large new markets for steel.

These fluctuating and varying markets, which come and go and shift their geographical centers, present U. S. Steel with changing problems. Since transportation is a large factor in the price at which steel can be sold, mills must be located as near as possible to the source of raw materials, with a practical eye turned to the accessibility of markets and transportation lines to carry the products to them.

Furthermore, the operation of steel plants is not simply a matter of producing a thing called steel in varying amounts, depending on the demand. Steel is made in thousands of varieties to meet the exacting needs of numerous industries. New steels are constantly required for specific purposes, and the research men of the steel industry must find ways to make them. Practically every lot of steel produced in a mill is made to a customer's order for one of his products. In 1910, eleven standard steels did the job for the automobile industry. Now it uses 162 different kinds of steel in more than 1,000 combinations of shape, size and analysis.

THE JOB OF U. S. STEEL

The job of U. S. Steel is to supply its customers with the kinds of steel required, in the amounts needed, and as promptly as possible, in a dynamic, expanding economy such as we have in the United States. A steel company has the difficult task of competing in a "heavy" industry, which must be "on its toes" to make the moves required to furnish the basic metal of this age, where and when it is needed.

During its fifty years, U. S. Steel has grown and prospered because it has been "on its toes" to serve the steel markets of the nation as they have developed.

In the early part of the century, the Corporation's manufacture of basic steel was confined largely to plants in Middle Western and Northeastern states, where it was practical to use iron ore from the rich ore fields of the Lake Superior region. Furthermore, manufacturing industries were concentrated mostly in these states and furnished the major markets for products of the steel mills.

BUILDING THE PLANT AND CITY OF GARY

As the present century got under way, the Middle West began to rival the East as a manufacturing region. U. S. Steel had steel-producing plants in and near the bustling city of Chicago. In keeping with the Corporation's policy of endeavoring to meet regional steel needs, it was decided in 1905 to construct a new steel-producing plant in the Chicago area for the expanding Middle Western market.

A few miles from Chicago, in Indiana, about

Gary Works, world's largest integrated steel mill, a monument to Judge Gary, U. S. Steel's chief founder.

9,000 acres of sand dunes, with a ten-mile frontage on Lake Michigan, were acquired. Here, U. S. Steel constructed a large integrated steel mill with the most up-to-date facilities then existing and built a model city with homes for employees, playgrounds, schools and other public buildings. The city was named Gary, in honor of Judge Elbert H. Gary, then Chairman of the Board. Ground was broken in August 1906, and by 1911 the plant, city and railroad terminal had been virtually completed at a cost of some $80,000,000. Gary Works has since been enlarged and modernized and is today the world's largest single integrated steel mill, with the capacity to produce 6,000,000 tons of steel annually. It is a monument to the man whose foresight envisaged its construction.

U. S. Steel's subsidiary near Birmingham has been identified with the city's growth as a great steel center.

STEEL FOR THE SOUTH

The region near Birmingham, Alabama, was destined by nature to become a great iron and steel center. Generous amounts of iron ore, coking coal and limestone exist there in closer proximity than in any other part of the United States. Although the presence of these natural resources was known in the early nineteenth century, only sporadic attempts were made to utilize them in the manufacture of iron until the 1860's. A group of enterprising Alabamians, foreseeing the eventual development of a large iron and general manufacturing industry based on these mineral deposits, founded a community in 1871 and prophetically named it Birmingham after the great steel city in England.

The infant iron industry and Birmingham developed together. Steel was first produced in the Birmingham district in 1888, but in a small amount,

Strip steel for cotton bale ties, one of many U. S. Steel products made in the South for southern agriculture.

and the metal was made in that area on a limited scale until the Tennessee Coal, Iron and Railroad Company constructed a modern steel plant with a capacity of 1,000 ingot tons a day and tapped its furnaces for the first time on November 30, 1899.

Tennessee Coal, Iron and Railroad Company originated in Tennessee in 1860, and moved to the vicinity of Birmingham in 1886. In the years following the construction of its first steel plant, the company developed into the largest steel producer in the South and became prominently identified with the growth of Birmingham as a great steel center.

A SOUTHERN SUBSIDIARY IS ACQUIRED

In 1905, a syndicate acquired a majority of the capital stock of the company and planned an extensive enlargement program by which the ingot and rail capacity would be doubled. Construction of the new facilities was still under way when the financial panic of 1907 struck the nation. Numerous banks and trust companies failed throughout the United States. Credit was virtually suspended.

Tennessee Coal, Iron and Railroad Company then had a floating debt of $4,000,000 and an expert who had recently appraised the company's plants estimated that it would take $20,000,000 to put the company on a sound financial and competitive basis— a sum of money the syndicate was not prepared to advance. This adverse condition of the company, aggravated by the panic, caused a severe depreciation in the value of the company's stock. As a consequence of this, one of the chief brokerage houses of New York, which held large quantities of the stock as collateral, was in dire financial straits. If the brokerage house should fail, it was feared that this would greatly intensify the panic and cause a chain reaction of many other business failures. With the purpose of warding off such a disaster, representations were made to Judge Gary that U. S. Steel buy the properties of Tennessee Coal, Iron and Railroad Company, which would restore the value of the company's stock.

Judge Gary rejected the proposal. As the financial panic tightened its grip on the nation and the salutary effects of the purchase were insistently pressed upon him, Judge Gary finally yielded, but only on condition that the entire matter be put before President Theodore Roosevelt. This was done in an overnight visit to Washington by Judge Gary and Henry C. Frick. The President voiced approval of the project, a position later sustained by the Attorney

General and the United States Supreme Court. The purchase was completed on November 1, 1907.

Large sums of money have since been spent by U. S. Steel in modernizing and diversifying the products of this southern subsidiary. Identifying itself intimately with the economy of the South, the Tennessee Coal, Iron and Railroad Company has been part and parcel of the phenomenal progress in southern agriculture and industry.

THE TWENTIES AND THIRTIES

In the years following World War I a revolution was taking place in our national economy which precipitated a corresponding revolution in the steel industry. The country was moving from a capital goods economy to a consumption economy. Mass production of automobiles, radios, washing machines, vacuum cleaners and other consumer products, by raising living standards, widened the markets for the whole range of consumer goods. Most of the manufactured consumer products, especially the all-steel automobile body, required large tonnages of sheet and strip steel.

Existing methods for rolling sheets could not produce them in either quantity or quality to meet the new needs. It is here that a great change in the steel industry took place. To meet the challenge, it developed the continuous wide hot strip mill, followed shortly by the cold reduction mill. The latter improves the product so that it may be more readily and economically shaped in heavy stamping presses into complicated forms.

The radical change that was occurring in our economy and in the steel industry may be seen in the following figures: At the time U. S. Steel was formed, steel rails amounted to 23 per cent of national steel production for sale; by 1928-1929 they had dropped to roughly eight per cent, and by 1936 to three and a half per cent. On the other hand,

Myron C. Taylor, during whose Chairmanship far-reaching changes took place in U. S. Steel operations.

sheet and strip, which constituted but six and a half per cent of national steel production for sale early in the century, rose to 19 per cent in the 1928-1929 period and to 31 per cent in 1936.

To keep abreast of the new market demands, U. S. Steel began to install continuous wide hot strip mills in the 1920's, followed in the 1930's by the cold reduction mills. The greatest change in the Corporation's operations took place in a ten-year period, from 1928 to 1938, under the Chairmanship of Myron C. Taylor. In those years, numerous obsolete plants were disposed of, others were modernized and new ones were added at a total cost of over half a billion dollars. In 1937, scarcely one-quarter of United States Steel's products was of the same composition or made in the same way as in 1928.

GROWING WITH THE WEST

The Far West has grown tremendously in the past

41

decade, both industrially and in population, requiring increased tonnages of steel. Just before World War II, the Pacific Coast region produced only 28 per cent of the 2,200,000 tons of finished steel which it consumed. Three years after the war, it produced 56 per cent of its finished steel consumption. U. S. Steel has had an important share in doubling the proportion of locally-produced steel in the seven Western states during this period. As a matter of fact, since 1930, when the Corporation began to produce steel in the West, its annual ingot capacity has expanded at a rate five and one half times the rate of population growth.

When U. S. Steel, twenty years ago, decided that it could best discharge its responsibilities to Western customers by producing steel on the Pacific Coast, it purchased the Columbia Steel Company which had been founded in California in 1910. Iron

More steel for the West. Left, a modern addition to U. S. Steel's facilities in the vicinity of San Francisco.

Geneva Works, Geneva, Utah, built at Government's request in World War II and since acquired by U. S. Steel.

for conversion into steel is obtained by Columbia's mines and facilities in Utah, a third area where the necessary raw materials are found in sufficient quantities for steel production. As a member of U. S. Steel's industrial family, Columbia Steel Company has greatly improved and enlarged its facilities near San Francisco and Los Angeles to supply steel for manufacturing plants, agriculture, canning, lumbering and other industries on the Pacific Coast.

UTAH, NEW STEEL CENTER

The Corporation's steel production in the West, for the West, has been considerably augmented by the establishment of a large new steel center in Utah. During World War II, the need arose for a greatly increased supply of steel plates and special forms of structural steel for the construction of ships on the Pacific Coast where the largest volume of merchant ships was being built. To meet the emergency demand, the Government decided to build a large, integrated steel mill in Utah and called upon the engineering and operating experience of U. S. Steel to construct and operate it. The site chosen was Geneva, near Salt Lake City. There, U. S. Steel constructed and operated for the Government, without charge or fee, the largest steel mill west of the Mississippi.

At the end of the war, when the Government asked the various members of the steel industry about their interest in acquiring the Geneva plant, U. S. Steel indicated a willingness to make an offer for its lease or purchase. When some members of the War Surplus Board objected, U. S. Steel withdrew. Intense disappointment spread through the Intermountain and Pacific Coast States, where the belief was almost universal that only a strong company such as U. S. Steel, with ample resources and know-how, could successfully operate a plant as large as Geneva.

In a spontaneous movement, chambers of commerce, trade associations, labor organizations, civic groups, and others began a concentrated drive to persuade U. S. Steel to reconsider its position. This drive "took on the proportions of a crusade" by which U. S. Steel was eventually "dragged into the bidding," according to Senator Arthur V. Watkins, of Utah.

When the Geneva plant was put up for sale at competitive bidding by the Government in 1946, U. S. Steel, in response to widespread demand and requests from Government officials, entered a bid. The Corporation offered $40,000,000 for the plant and pledged to spend at least $18,600,000 additional toward peacetime reconversion of the Geneva plant, including facilities for the production of hot rolled strip for final processing in the new modern $25,000,000 cold reduction mill to be built at the Pittsburg, California, plant of Columbia Steel Company.

U. S. Steel's bid was the highest received and was accepted by the Government. The sale of the Geneva plant to U. S. Steel was approved by Attorney General Tom C. Clark as not violating the anti-trust laws. Accordingly, on June 19, 1946, the Geneva plant joined U. S. Steel's family. It has since been operated by Geneva Steel Company, the same subsidiary that operated the plant for the Government during the war.

Commenting on the sale, Senator Watkins said that "the entire West has benefited and will continue to benefit by reason of the purchase of the Geneva steel plant by the United States Steel Corporation. For the first time in history, the Intermountain and Pacific Coast States were placed on a competitive basis with the rest of the United States . . . The sale of Geneva plant to United States Steel Corporation is making it possible for the establishment of numerous fabricating enterprises in the Western States. . . . Out of these industries should come employment for hundreds of thousands of American citizens and an increased production of necessary commodities."

SERVING THE NATION

From the foregoing, it may be seen that U. S. Steel is indeed "The Industrial Family That Serves the Nation." As its activities have become diversified to serve the changing steel needs of the nation, new members have been added to U. S. Steel's family. The services rendered by these companies and their contributions to the economic progress of the nation are described in succeeding chapters. The principal subsidiaries are listed on page 221.

UNITED STATES STEEL COMPANY

The most important change in the corporate structure of U. S. Steel in recent years took place on January 1, 1951. For purposes of simplifying the corporate structure, a single company was formed of four wholly-owned subsidiaries: U. S. Steel Corporation of Delaware, Carnegie-Illinois Steel Corporation, H. C. Frick Coke Company and United States Coal and Coke Company. The new company is called United States Steel Company. Its headquarters are in Pittsburgh.

U. S. Steel Corporation of Delaware had previously functioned, in an advisory capacity, as an over-all coordinator of operations conducted by the raw material, steel-producing, distributing and fabricating subsidiaries. Carnegie-Illinois Steel Corporation, U. S. Steel's largest subsidiary until January 1, 1951, was organized in 1935 following consolidation of Carnegie Steel Company with other subsidiaries and the acquisition of properties of Illinois Steel Company, all acquired when U. S. Steel was formed. The H. C. Frick Coke Company and the United States Coal and Coke Company were U. S. Steel's coal-mining subsidiaries, supplying metallurgical coal for operations in the Pittsburgh and Chicago districts and other points in the northeastern section of the United States.

PRESENT LEADERSHIP OF U. S. STEEL

Since the retirement of Myron C. Taylor as Chairman of the Board of Directors on April 5, 1938, the responsibilities reposing in the top executive function of U. S. Steel have been shared by three officers:

Chairman of the Board of Directors: Irving S. Olds since June 4, 1940, when he succeeded Edward R. Stettinius, Jr., who resigned on that date to enter Government service, eventually becoming Secretary of State. Mr. Stettinius was elected Chairman on April 5, 1938.

President: Benjamin F. Fairless, who was elected to that office on January 1, 1938, after serving for three years as President of Carnegie-Illinois Steel Corporation. Mr. Fairless is also President of the largest operating subsidiary, United States Steel Company.

Chairman of the Finance Committee: Enders M. Voorhees, who was elected to that position on April 5, 1938.

The Chairman of the Board exercises a general oversight of the conduct of the business and affairs of the Corporation. It is his responsibility to see that all orders and resolutions of the Board of Directors are carried into effect by the proper officers. In connection with these policy duties, the Chairman has general charge and supervision of the public relations of the Corporation.

The President is the Chief Administrative Officer of U. S. Steel. His jurisdiction is primarily over production and sales.

The Chairman of the Finance Committee guides the financial destinies of the Corporation.

In actual practice these three officers work closely together on all matters affecting the policy and administration of U. S. Steel.

CHAPTER THREE

TWO WORLD WARS

On two occasions, the brain power, the man power and the machine power of U. S. Steel have been thrown without stint or reserve into the production of steel, the sinews of war, to help defend the freedom of America and our democratic form of government.

Both World Wars settled down, in the long run, to a battle of industrial production. The might of America's economic machine, thrown into the conflict, ultimately settled the issue in each case. In World War I, the emergency value of large, efficient industrial units was demonstrated for the first time. They switched from making

articles of peace to making articles of war and produced them in such quantities that the Allied Forces were able to bring Kaiser Wilhelm's armies to their knees.

World War II was essentially the same story, except that production was on a vastly greater scale for a war of global dimensions. For magnitude and speed of production, the record of private industry in World War II is unsurpassed in history. At a time when France was prostrate under

American victory parade, leaving the Arch of Triumph, Champs-Élysées, Paris, after the close of World War II.

General John J. Pershing, after World War I victory, rides at the head of his troops down the same avenue.

Hitler and Great Britain was constantly under the merciless bombings of the *Luftwaffe*, and the Russians were reeling under the first Nazi onslaughts, America changed from a peace footing to the Arsenal of Democracy and more than doubled its industrial output, producing over 186 billion dollars worth of ships, planes, guns and other war materiel in five years, from July 1, 1940 to July 31, 1945.

STEEL IN THE FIRST WORLD WAR

The production feats of American industry in both wars depended in the last analysis on an adequate supply of steel. The struggles of democracy against oppression thus became fundamentally a War of Steel. When Kaiser Wilhelm threw his legions into Belgium on August 4, 1914, Germany and her ally, the Austro-Hungarian Empire, were producing steel at the rate of 17,600,000 tons a year, compared to 21,340,000 tons by the United Kingdom, France, Luxembourg, Belgium, Russia, Poland, Italy and Canada, who were soon arrayed against them. The United States in 1914 produced 26,335,000 tons of

Americans attacking in World War I. Both wars became a war of industrial production, based on steel.

steel, which was nearly nine million tons more than that backing the Kaiser's war machine.

As the war progressed, the United States Government began to take defensive measures which included greater steel production. The American steel industry responded energetically and in 1917, the year in which we entered the conflict, had almost doubled its production, bringing it to 50,468,000 tons. The tremendous weight of American war industries tipped the scales decisively in favor of the Allies. During the war, steel production declined somewhat in enemy nations and in some of the Allied countries, notably Belgium and France. How the Russian and Polish steel industries fared during the German invasion of those countries is not known. Even so, omitting figures for Russian and Polish production, the Allies in the final year of World War I supported their war effort by a production of approximately 66,500,000 tons of steel, of which nearly 50,-000,000 tons came from American steel mills, while the enemy's war potential was reduced to 16,600,000 tons of steel. On the day of victory, the Allies were turning out more than four times as much steel as the enemy.

From 1915 onward, U. S. Steel alone delivered more steel each year than Germany and Austria-Hungary combined. In five war years, from 1914 to 1918, inclusive, the output of the Corporation's subsidiaries amounted to 99,700,000 tons of steel.

AMERICA'S GROWTH BETWEEN THE TWO WARS

World War I absorbed the productive energies of our people on farms and in factories all over the land. But economically speaking, we were not the same nation at all when World War II broke out. Between 1914 and 1939, our national income increased from 33.9 billion dollars to more than 72 billion dollars. In 1914, America manufactured less than 550,000 passenger automobiles annually. After World War I, we became accustomed to three, and even more than four million passenger cars a year coming from the automotive assembly lines. The manufacture of many consumer products, especially for the home, such as radios, washing machines, vacuum cleaners, mechanical refrigerators, toasters and others, really got under way in mass production quantities for the first time. To supply the new markets, the steel industry expanded and modernized its equipment and on May 10, 1939, when Hitler's blitzkrieg struck Western Europe like a thunderclap, the steel mills of this country had reached an annual capacity of 81,600,000 tons of steel. This, alone, illustrates the degree of America's economic expansion between the two wars.

PROVIDENTIAL PEACETIME EXPANSION IN STEEL

The Axis Powers of Germany and Italy in 1939 were backed by an annual steel capacity of 27,900,000 tons, opposed by a capacity of 38,200,000 tons on the part of Great Britain, France, Belgium, Luxembourg and Poland. The Axis Powers, including Japan, at the height of their conquests attained an estimated steel capacity of roughly 75,000,000 tons a year, which was a little short of American capacity when the war began. In the Axis camp were the steel industries of captive France, Belgium, Luxembourg and Poland.

It is worth recalling this situation, with its hazards to the security of this nation, in view of the fact that only a few years earlier the 81,600,000-ton steel capacity of the United States was termed "excessive" in some quarters of Washington. By the summer of 1941, however, when Britain was the last bastion of liberty in Europe, and ominous warlike signs were evident in Japan,

the American Government with great urgency asked the steel industry to expand its capacity by 10,000,000 tons in the shortest possible time.

No company in a private enterprise system likes to have capacity on its hands which it cannot use competitively. A steel company gears its plants for what, in its experienced judgment, is sufficient to take care of its anticipated market demand. It was providential for the security of the United States, after Pearl Harbor, that U. S. Steel and other steel companies had acted on their own realistic appraisal of the country's peacetime steel needs and had expanded their capacities accordingly. The $600,-000,000 spent by U. S. Steel in enlarging and improving its facilities from 1929 to 1940 to make more and better steels for peacetime, turned out to be a farsighted investment in national security when the bombs fell on Pearl Harbor, because it saved time—that priceless element of warfare. It takes two to three years to build a steel mill. If estimates of the country's steel needs, reached in cloistered committee rooms by inexperienced critics, had been followed and the "excessive" capacity had been cut back in 1939 or 1940, the United States would have been seriously handicapped after Decem-

After the attack on Pearl Harbor, American steel production expanded rapidly to supply the needs of war.

ber 7, 1941, when shipyards clamored for steel plates, aircraft plants for special steels, and our entire defense program called for steel, and yet more steel, for guns, munitions, tanks and trucks.

In response to the Government's request in 1941, the steel industry of America pitched in and built new furnaces, rolling mills and finishing equipment. Completely new steel mills were constructed.

LOW PROFITS IN WARTIME

In every respect war is costly to a nation. It is costly, most of all, in lives. It is costly to the nation in the suspension of peacetime production, which takes years to overcome, as we have seen since 1945. War puts a burden on every citizen through the increased public debt.

What Hitler thought impossible—D-Day landings on the Normandy beaches by the Allies, June 6, 1944.

Some obsolete mills were called back into service. Year by year the steel capacity rose until it reached a record-breaking total of 95,500,000 tons in 1945. This was 20,000,000 more tons than the maximum steel capacity at any time of our combined enemies.

Steel production mounted in proportion. To supply the basic metal for war, the steel plants of America by 1944 had increased their output 70 per cent over 1939 and produced from January 1, 1940 to August 15, 1945, a grand total of 467,300,000 tons of steel. U. S. Steel alone, poured out 161,000,000 tons of steel from its furnaces during the same period.

From a business standpoint, war is costly to large corporations which normally realize a far larger profit in years of peace. In the ten-year period, 1941-1950, inclusive, America suffered five years of war and enjoyed five years of peace. During the latter period U. S. Steel's profits averaged 6.3 cents per dollar of sales, but were only 4.1 cents per sales dollar in the war years—about one-third less in war than in peace. The profits of other large American corporations were also lower during the war.

D-DAY AND MASS PRODUCTION

For the fabrication of steel into tanks, guns, planes and thousands of other implements of war, and in the construction of ships, American industry was ready to do the job as it could be done nowhere else in the world. It takes men accustomed to thinking in big terms to have the vision and ability to do things on a big scale. If ever such men were needed, it was in the second World War and perhaps at no time more urgently than in the planning and preparation for D-Day, June 6, 1944, when the Allied

over open beaches and sustain it with supplies, and had based their main defenses on the seaports. But the impossible was accomplished.

Within twenty days after the first landings, one million men and their supplies were ashore in France. Within 109 days, the Allies had put ashore nearly two and a half million men and more than half a million vehicles, or four vehicles every

Armies invaded Normandy.

D-Day required boldness, vision, enterprise and managerial skill of the highest order, backed by the industrial prowess of America. Some of our political and military friends abroad looked with misgivings on the American plan to land in force on the Normandy beaches and doubted if it could be done. In the end, they were persuaded to our point of view and joined wholeheartedly in the undertaking.

Consider what was accomplished by the Allied Armies under the leadership of General Dwight D. Eisenhower, Supreme Commander. An armada of 4,000 ships set out for the beaches of Normandy on that fateful night of June 5th. The Germans had thought it impossible for the Allies to land an army

Destruction by a 4-day hurricane on Normandy coast was soon made up by American productive capacity.

minute, day and night. In the same period, some 17,000,000 tons of weapons and supplies were pushed across the open beaches and through the battered port of Cherbourg—more than twice the total General Pershing received through open friendly ports in the first nineteen months of World War I.

On June 19, a hurricane struck the English Channel and the Normandy coast and raged for four days, halting all sea communications with Britain and hurling numerous ships and small vessels onto the beach. Commenting on the damage caused by the hurricane, General Eisenhower wrote in his book, "Crusade in Europe": "There was no sight in the war that so impressed me with the industrial might of America as the wreckage on the landing beaches. To any other nation the disaster would have been almost decisive; but so great was America's productive capacity that the great storm occasioned little more than a ripple in the development of our build-up."

AIRPOWER, HITLER'S DOOM

D-Day was an epic. The avalanche of weapons and supplies from the factories of America, supporting the assault, marked the beginning of the end of Hitler. The landings and lodgment of Allied Forces might have been far more costly if mass production of aircraft in the United States had not made it possible for the Allies to dominate the air completely so that the Nazi air force did not appear. At one time, a sky train of airborne troops 200 miles long crossed the English Channel. Three German Field Marshals—Hermann Goering, Karl von Rundstedt and Albert Kesselring—stated on their capture that the chief single reason for Germany's collapse was the Allied air superiority—a tribute to the businesses, large and small, that produced 297,000 airplanes in five war years.

SPEEDY MOBILIZATION OF LARGE INDUSTRIES

There is another aspect of large industries that may well be a crucial factor in a national emergency. That is the speed with which they can mobilize their productive forces. General Nathan Forrest, Confederate cavalry leader, once said victory goes to the side that can "get thar fustest with the mostest." But the men must be armed to fight and they must be reinforced constantly with sup-

plies. World War II might have lasted longer and cost many more American lives if our industries had been in little piecemeal sections when the Japanese bombs disabled every battleship and numerous other naval vessels in Pearl Harbor and knocked out most of our air force in the Hawaiian area. Within a week we were also at war with Germany and Italy.

Every day counted in the speedy mobilization of our industrial resources. Only companies with the facilities and know-how for manufacturing steel,

Allied air superiority was chief single reason for Germany's collapse, according to Nazi Field Marshals.

"When Hitler put his war on wheels he ran it right down our alley"—Lt. General Brehon B. Somervell.

automobiles, refrigerators, tractors, and other products in large volume could turn around and produce steel, tanks, military trucks, guns and other war materiel in mammoth proportions, as our industries did, until the torrent of equipment and supplies made the United States Army and Navy the most powerful and destructive war machine the world had ever known.

Fortunately, when every passing day was of critical importance, large integrated steel companies, such as U. S. Steel, were in existence, with iron ore and coal mines, limestone quarries, ore vessels, coke ovens, furnaces, rolling and finishing mills and fabricating plants. Administered by U. S. Steel's experienced management, these physical resources could swing into production as a close-knit team more rapidly than if they were disjointed units.

"RIGHT DOWN OUR ALLEY"

World War I was fought largely from trenches. In the second conflict, warfare caught up with the machine. It was a kind of warfare particularly suited to the genius of America. As Lieutenant General Brehon B. Somervell, Commanding General of the U. S. Army Service Forces in the war, summed it up: "When Hitler put his war on wheels he ran it right down our alley." America showed the world a blitzkrieg that moved faster and struck harder than anything Hitler ever dreamed of. A typical division had mechanical equipment equal to nearly 200,000 horsepower, or 50 times as much as in 1917.

Motorized units gave our military divisions the advantage of greater mobility. In Hitler's vaunted "panzer armies," the regular infantry divisions, early in the war, were still transported mostly by horses. General George C. Marshall, Chief of Staff of the U. S. Army during the war, wrote in his biennial report, covering 1943 to 1945: "The United States, profiting from the mass production achievements

of its automotive industry, made all its forces truck-drawn and had enough trucks left over to supply the British armies with large numbers of motor vehicles and send tremendous quantities to the Red Army."

General Eisenhower remarked in "Crusade in Europe" that the mobility of American land forces was vastly increased by the "mass production methods of American industry. There was certainly no nation in the world that could have supplied, repaired and supported the great fleet of motor transportation that the American armed forces used in World War II."

Armor plate sections for tanks being cut to exact dimensions by flame-cutting units in a U. S. Steel mill.

BLITZKRIEG—A WAR OF ALLOY STEEL

Mechanized warfare presented the American steel industry with a different problem from that faced in World War I. In general, wherever wheels turned, the steel had to be stronger and tougher in World War II in order to stand up and perform under the gruelling conditions of rough terrain and in the varied climates and temperatures of global warfare. Defensively, tanks and warships required heavier and tougher armor. Offensively, armor-piercing shells had to have deeper penetrating power. Special steels were needed for oxygen tanks, engines, fire walls, exhaust systems and other vital parts of aircraft. The steels for practically all of these purposes were alloy steels. In fact, nearly every major and minor piece of equipment in World War II used alloy steel, the "super-steel," which in peacetime comprises about six per cent of total steel production. This made the war not merely a War of Steel, but more particularly a War of Alloy Steel.

Steel for the blitzkrieg had to be tougher than in World War I, requiring alloy steels in most cases.

As the demands for alloy steel increased, stockpiles of strategic alloying metals began to dwindle with alarming rapidity. Due to Axis conquests and sinkings of cargo ships, stockpiles of certain metals could not be adequately replenished.

America's entire war effort was in jeopardy. If we continued to consume our reserves of alloying metals in the same proportions as before, there was enough to make only a portion of the large tonnages of alloy steel required for the war production pro-

gram. Metallurgists of American industry jumped into the breach and saved the day. Headed by a metallurgist from U. S. Steel, a special committee of metallurgists from various steel companies was charged by the War Production Board to find a way to stretch our scant reserves of critical alloying metals and still make steel that measured up to the stiff requirements of the Army and Navy.

PEACETIME RESEARCH PAYS OFF

Making use of its long experience in developing better steels for peacetime, the committee found that by using two, three or even four of the alloying elements available in larger amounts through the use of alloy steel scrap, rather than larger percentages of one or two as in the past, it was possible to produce alloy steels entirely suitable for war purposes. But for this brilliant and timely contribution by the steel industry's metallurgists, America would have been at a serious disadvantage in fighting the war.

The foregoing example strikingly illustrates the value to national security of industrial research in peacetime for new and improved products. The United States had at its disposal not only the world's most highly developed industrial machine, manned by skilled workers, but also the largest staff of research specialists maintained by private industry anywhere in the world. In civilian capacities and in uniform, this battalion of scientists was invaluable to the Army and the Navy in tackling the hosts of problems presented by modern warfare.

In his biennial report, General Marshall wrote: "In the years of peace between the two world wars we permitted Germany to far outpace us in the development of instruments which might have military use." Although we had a late start, we overtook Germany in most weapons and surpassed her in many. It is probably fair to say that the reason we could do so is because a people who had the ingenuity, enterprise and creative imagination to achieve the highest living standards in the world, when compelled to defend the freedoms that made such achievements possible, were able to pour forth a crushing superiority in implements of war that overwhelmed their enemies.

SOME WARTIME CONTRIBUTIONS OF U. S. STEEL

The research and technological knowledge acquired by U. S. Steel from 1929 to 1940 at a cost in excess of $90,000,000 saved precious time in the solution of many problems which the Army and Navy brought to the Corporation during World War II. A few, among many, may be cited.

THE BEST HELMET IN THE WORLD

Steel for the G.I.'s helmet had to be tougher and withstand greater fire power than the helmet of World War I. The Army's specifications required steel of virtually contradictory properties. The difficulties were mastered by U. S. Steel's metallurgists, who developed methods of producing an alloy steel which combined all of the qualities specified by the Army, so that American fighting men were protected by the best helmet in the world.

STEEL LANDING MATS FOR PLANES

In World War II, when the quick use of air power was required to provide aerial cover for our fast-moving troops, the perforated steel landing mat helped to put the blitz in our own type of lightning war. The design and chief development of the mat were done by Carnegie-Illinois Steel Corporation,

U. S. Steel subsidiary, now a part of U. S. Steel Company. The invention was freely shared with other companies. At one time 28 other manufacturers were producing the steel mat.

SPRINGS FOR AIRCRAFT CANNONS

When the Germans mounted 75 mm. cannons in some of their planes, the U. S. Air Force had to do likewise in order to match them in the air. There was no existing spring that could handle the gun's terrific recoil action in the small space available for the spring. The problem was tossed into the lap of spring experts at the American Steel & Wire Company, a U. S. Steel subsidiary. After intensive research they delivered a spring that did the trick, thus enabling our flyers to fight on equal terms with cannon-equipped Nazi planes.

BOMB SPINNING

Another technological triumph of U. S. Steel was the development of the "bomb spinning" method which made it possible to double the production rate of bombs. Copied by over 200 bomb manufacturers, it was an important factor in sending a steady stream of bombs to U. S. Army and Navy Air Forces, who were dropping 4,400 tons of missiles a day in late 1944. The "bomb spinning" method was not worked out in a day or a month. It was the result of years of peacetime experimentation by U. S. Steel's National Tube Company, which had successfully applied the device in closing the ends of steel pressure cylinders.

SAVING STEEL IN SHELLS

In experiments on artillery shells for large guns, National Tube Company developed a method by which the stock for 155 mm. shell forgings could be reduced by 20 pounds—20 pounds of steel that could be used for other war purposes. On this basis, one subsidiary alone, Tennessee Coal, Iron and Railroad Company, of Birmingham, saved the Government 44,000 tons of steel in the manufacture of 4,600,000 shell forgings.

THE BRIDGE OF SHIPS

Urgent as it was to produce weapons and munitions in mass quantities, they were of no value until they reached the fighting fronts. A bewildering diversity and volume of supplies—700,000 separate articles in all—had to cross the Atlantic and Pacific Oceans to sustain American armies in World War II. Also, through Lend-Lease, the United States helped to fortify the home and fighting fronts of our Allies.

America faced a number of emergencies in World

Steel aircraft landing mat, U. S. Steel invention, the "outstanding development of the year in aviation."

G. I.'s were protected by the toughest steel helmet ever made — a metallurgical triumph of U. S. Steel.

Spinning the nose of an aircraft bomb in a U. S. Steel plant, a method which doubled the production rate.

Bombs for loading into a Superfortress. Day and night bombing by U. S. Air Forces helped to shorten the war.

Cleaning a 75 mm. cannon in a B-25, while man at the right readies the shells, before a bombing mission.

Allied convoy heads for a battlefront. Record-breaking ship construction gave America the needed vessels.

War II, but perhaps none was more critical than during the first year of the war when ship sinkings by Axis submarines far exceeded construction in American shipyards. The tenuous life line of shipping to our armed forces abroad and to our Allies hung by a slender thread. There was a period in 1943 and 1944 when shipbuilding consumed 21 per cent of all the steel produced in this country—considerably more steel than any other branch of the war effort.

American shipbuilding and allied industries performed a prodigious feat in constructing the mightiest navy and the largest merchant marine that ever sailed the seas under the flag of any nation. In five war years, a total of 5,425 merchant vessels of 53,200,000 deadweight tons slid down the ways of American shipyards. In six top months of World War II as much merchant tonnage was constructed as during three peak years of the first World War. From July 1, 1940 to July 31, 1945, the U. S. Navy added 71,060 ships to its fleet, of which 1,201 were combat ships, 64,500 were landing and assault ships. The remainder were auxiliaries and other craft.

RACE AGAINST TIME

The crucial race against time in building the bridge of ships began in the steel mills of America. During the most critical period of submarine warfare, the United States had the capacity to produce but half of the steel plates and armor required for the Merchant Marine and Navy shipbuilding programs. To double capacity by erecting new plants would have taken about two years. Meanwhile, almost daily American and Allied ships with their precious cargoes were going to the bottom of the ocean. Something like a miracle was called for and it was accomplished.

Mention has been made in these pages of the continuous hot strip mills introduced into the steel industry during the 1920's. The steel sheets produced on these mills are relatively thin—less than three-sixteenths of an inch thick—and far from heavy enough to serve as plates for ship hulls or as armor for battleships. Designed to roll and handle light sheets for peacetime, it was never considered possible that these mills could roll heavy plates for ships.

But engineers of the Carnegie-Illinois Steel Corporation found ways to convert sheet mills into plate mills, and they did it in record time. Five weeks after conversion began, plates were being delivered for the bridge of ships! Largely through this conversion, U. S. Steel was able to increase its plate production four times and to supply about 40 per cent of all the plates rolled in this country. In another emergency, U. S. Steel served the shipbuilding program. This was the construction, at the Government's request, of a large, integrated steel mill near Salt Lake City, Utah, to roll plates and structural shapes for the West Coast shipbuilding yards.

U. S. Steel also built ships—911 in all—including destroyers, destroyer escorts, cruisers, landing vessels, troopships and others. Federal Shipbuilding and Dry Dock Company, the shipbuilding subsidiary, sold since the war to the Navy, reduced the construction time of destroyers from eighteen months in 1939 to four and three-fourths months in 1943 and was the first yard ever to launch four destroyers in one day. Another member of U. S. Steel's family, American Bridge Company, applying its long experience in structural work, reduced the building time for LST's from 260 days in 1943 to 63 days in 1944. The shorter period, attained early in 1944, was of momentous aid to the Government because the LST's then being rushed to completion in the yard were for the D-Day invasion, and the accomplishment won a tribute from the Navy for the company and the yard's 10,000 workers.

By these achievements and many others, United States Steel Corporation is proud to have served the defense of this nation in two World Wars.

U. S. Steel built 119 LST's—Landing Ships, Tanks— and reduced construction time from 260 to 63 days.

Launching a combat cargo vessel, one of 911 ships of various kinds built by U. S. Steel during the war.

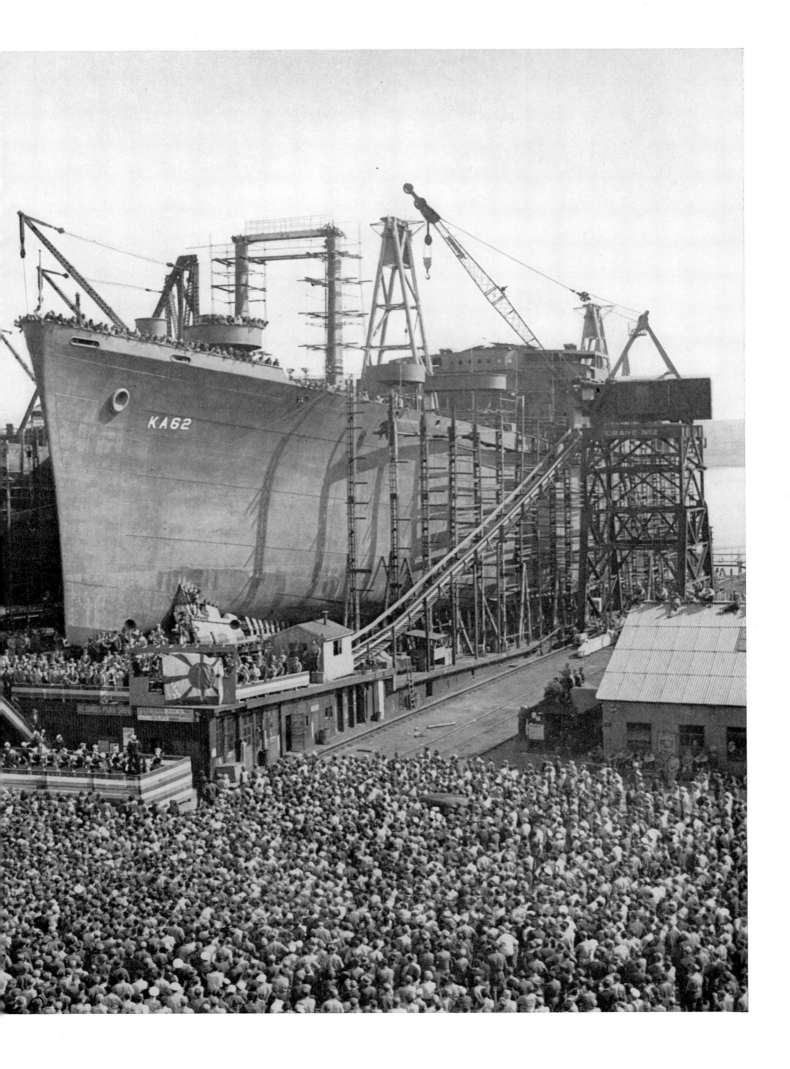

Stainless steel

Steel for auto fenders

Steel for rails

Steel for springs

CHAPTER FOUR

RESEARCH FOR PROGRESS AND SECURITY

Because steel is a basic metal, serving practically every industry, research in the steel industry is of fundamental importance. Hundreds of products we use today simply could not have come into existence until research developed new steels of special properties to do things that steel could never do before.

Although the essential principles of steelmaking remain virtually the same as at the beginning of the century, steel itself has changed so much that it hardly resembles that of fifty years ago. Our way of life in 1951, with faster and longer trains, mass-produced passenger automobiles and trucks, aircraft and numerous home appliances, could not exist with

By exposing the inner secrets of steel, the research technician has made it the most versatile material known to man. Four microphotographs, above, show how the internal structure of steel varies for different purposes.

the steels of 1901. If the basic processes of steelmaking are the same as before, what has caused these revolutionary changes in steel itself? The answer is the discoveries made by research technologists. With the aid of science and the microscope, the metallurgist has exposed many of the secrets of steel, and knowing them, he has in a sense, mastered the metal. He has learned how to juggle and rearrange the internal structure of steel so that he can make steel do almost anything he wants it to do. He can make it in thousands of varieties, with slight gradations, from very soft and ductile to extremely hard. He can make it especially strong and he can make it corrosion-resistant. He has made steel into the most versatile material at the command of man. The average person may hardly have his interest stirred to learn that a certain steel

Stainless steel sheets receive their final polishing. The wonder metal has opened up a world of new steel uses.

may contain so much nickel and so much chromium, but he is mightily interested in stainless steel which is made by the addition of these two alloying elements.

STAINLESS STEEL—THE MIRACLE METAL

Stainless steel has opened up a whole new world of steel uses. It benefits our health because of its sanitary value in the pasteurization of milk and the manufacture of drugs, and when used in dental, medical and kitchen equipment. In addition to its corrosion-resistant properties, stainless steel is unusually strong and can withstand very high temperatures.

That is why it is in the fire walls, exhaust systems and turbo-superchargers of aircraft.

Stainless steel was first developed in England and Germany. U. S. Steel was among the three or four pioneers who undertook its development on a commercial scale in the United States. At first there were only two varieties, but now there are many. Over the years, U. S. Steel has produced numerous grades, one of which was the first to be used in stainless steel streamlined trains. During World War II, U. S. Steel developed a new kind of stainless steel of extraordinary strength, called "Stainless W," which was particularly useful for machine parts and valves. At the request of the Government it was kept secret in the war years, but now it is finding wide usage and performing services formerly considered impossible.

One of the latest uses of stainless steel is in television sets. Originally, the large vacuum tubes

of television receiving sets were made of glass. But as people desired larger screens, the tubes grew in size until finally it posed a difficult problem to make them entirely of glass. Would it be possible to substitute thin strong steel for the glass in the conical section of the tube? In cooperation with a manufacturer of television sets, U. S. Steel conducted experiments which yielded a novel grade of stainless steel answering every need. The new steel reduced manufacturing costs and enabled the public to enjoy improved television.

COR-TEN—THE STEEL ECONOMIZER

There are various ways to conserve our natural resources. In the case of iron ore, U. S. Steel is making intensive research efforts to utilize the low-

Left above, stainless steel in drug manufacture illustrates the many uses of the metal for hygienic purposes.

Larger television screens were made possible by the use of a new grade of stainless steel in the vacuum tubes.

grade ores existing in great abundance in the Lake Superior region, thus easing the drain on richer but less plentiful ores. Oddly enough, one of the benefits of a new steel developed by U. S. Steel is the conservation of iron ore.

Research work on this new steel was begun in the early 1930's. It was realized that freight cars, trucks, buses, and many kinds of moving equipment carried around a lot of unnecessary weight in their frames and bodies. If a steel could be found stronger, weight for weight, than the structural steel being used, it would require less of the new steel and thereby reduce the dead weight of the vehicle, with a resulting increased useful life. Less dead weight would mean less expense in moving the vehicle.

U. S. Steel's research laboratories developed a low cost steel with the necessary qualities, including resistance to corrosion. It was named Cor-Ten steel. In the trade it is known as a low alloy, high strength steel. It was demonstrated that approximately three tons of Cor-Ten are equivalent to four tons of ordinary steel.

This weight-saving, corrosion-resistant steel has been utilized chiefly in the manufacture of railroad freight cars and, to a lesser extent, in streamlined passenger trains. The automobile industry also makes extensive use of Cor-Ten steel in heavy trucks, trailers, gasoline truck tanks, garbage trucks and buses. It has proven to be of great value in heavy earth-moving equipment such as bulldozers, power shovels, ditchers and graders. It is widely applied in mine cars and mine equipment. In all of these uses, less Cor-Ten is needed than ordinary steel, thus saving money all around and conserving essential raw materials—iron ore, coking coal and limestone. Since Cor-Ten usually outlasts ordinary steel, there is an added saving to the user of vehicles or equipment fabricated with this steel.

The number of U. S. Steel's research triumphs runs into the hundreds. Some have been described in connection with U. S. Steel's services in two World Wars. Other important research contributions are discussed in later chapters.

STEEL RESEARCH EMBRACES MANY FIELDS

The fields of research which the steel industry may be called upon to explore are almost limitless. Laboratories must be staffed and equipped to tackle a bewildering variety of problems. A long series of intimately related steps is involved in producing a ton of finished steel. A research problem may arise anywhere along the line—in the iron ore fields, the coal mines, the furnaces, the rolling mills, and in numerous finishing processes for a wide range of steel products. Each step in operations calls for the exercise of different talents by the research specialist. At the same time, studies are being constantly made into what might be called the science of steel, the composition and behavior of the metal, new varieties, and new processes for making them.

The tasks of research so far referred to are *internal* ones and they are practically exhaustless. But steel, being a basic metal, is sold to practically every kind of manufacturing industry, and the producer of steel must be familiar with the needs and problems of his customers and concern himself with them. An important part of steel research, therefore, is necessarily devoted to a study of the requirements of customers in order that each kind and grade of steel may perform the service demanded of it. This means that there must be staffs of scientists and technicians, who, between them, are capable of dealing expertly with problems relating to the use of steel in virtually every industry in the United States.

The U. S. Steel subsidiaries which manufacture steel pipe, for example, must have experts in their employ who can talk intelligently with engineers of an oil company about the flow of gas and liquids under pressure and offer authoritative advice on the best kind of steel to use. The specialists in steel sheets must be prepared to discuss this product in relation to stamping processes, enameling, plastic finishes, electrical transformers or building codes. It is not enough for U. S. Steel's authorities on tin plate to know all about its manufacture and to understand the operations in a container factory. In dealing with customers they may find themselves engaged in problems concerning the preservation of an extremely long and diversified list of foods and other products.

RESEARCH FOR THE CUSTOMERS' NEEDS

Frequently, the problem encountered by U. S. Steel and a customer cannot be solved by any existing steel or by the manufacturing processes being used by the customer. The problem then becomes the subject of research and experimentation. Many of the significant advances made during this century by U. S. Steel and other industries have come about in this way—by the joint efforts of the Corporation and its customers. Technological progress in other industries, particularly the automotive and home appliance industries, has been amazingly rapid. To keep abreast of their needs, the steel industry has moved in fast company and it has kept in step all the way.

To carry on such varied research activities requires a large staff of highly proficient men and extensive equipment. Scientists and technologists,

working in eight research laboratories and seventy other laboratories, conduct this vital work for U. S. Steel. Their efforts are supplemented by fellowships supported by U. S. Steel at numerous technical institutions and universities.

The resources of a large company are essential to maintain a research organization such as U. S. Steel's and to finance costly experiments over a long period of years. Not every project is successful and U. S. Steel has had its share of disappointing experiences, some of which have cost well over one million dollars.

A MAJOR RESEARCH TASK

The following research task of major proportions well illustrates the services that can be rendered by a company with a sufficient staff and adequate equipment. When alloy steels were first introduced on the market, relatively little was known about their many possible uses and behavior and no accepted stand-

Taking a moving picture of the fiery interior of a blast furnace, one of many research activities in steelmaking.

ards existed by which to judge them. As the demand for alloy steels increased, there was an insistent need for order and system to replace confusion.

U. S. Steel launched upon a systematic, comprehensive study of the influence of each alloying element on steel, singly and in combinations. Since nearly every form of steel undergoes what is termed "heat treatment" to bring out its maximum possibilities, an investigation was also made into the kind of heat treatment best suited to various grades of steel. The results of this monumental work were published in a book, 10,000 copies of which have been distributed without charge. So great has been the demand for this volume, that a revised and larger edition is being prepared.

The book constitutes one of the most valuable research contributions made to this nation in peace and in war by U. S. Steel. It is a metallurgical bible. By consulting it, a metallurgist can ascertain how to develop, in numerous alloy steels, the specified properties best suited for the job in hand. The practical application of its teachings by numerous industries in peacetime has borne fruit in hundreds of improved products of daily use which benefit our life in one way or another. The existence of the knowledge contained in the book was of crucial importance in World War II, when this country was threatened with a calamitous shortage of certain alloying elements needed to produce steel for modern warfare. The book's data on alloy steels were indispensable for the quick solution of the alloy steel problem which arose from the shortage of strategic alloying metals in World War II, related in the previous chapter.

RESEARCH AND SECURITY

Here, again, is demonstrated the value of industrial research, this time in relation to national security. Research is the wellspring of industrial progress, which makes for economic strength. In turn, economic strength is the bulwark of security. America was able to out-produce the Axis Powers and to perform technological miracles in World War II, because research and industry together had built up a powerful economic machine and had the technical knowl-

Laboratories are watchdogs of quality. Below, testing the breaking point of a steel rod, circled in blue.

Right, constant research by the steel industry contributes to progress in peace and to security in war.

edge and know-how at hand, developed under the incentives of competitive private enterprise. American industry and metallurgy were equal to the challenge. There can be no doubt whatsoever that had the steel industry been behind in research and technology, the results for this nation in that time of greatest need would have been disastrous.

CHAPTER FIVE

THE HUMAN ELEMENT

As human beings, we haven't changed much over the centuries, but how vastly changed is the world in which we live and the way we think about our relationships with each other! There was a time when man's thinking held it right and proper for a master to beat his servant and a person could be hanged for petty thievery. We now condemn those practices. Our *thinking* has changed.

In the present century, enlightened thinking on human relationships has progressed in many directions. The idea of women voting once appalled a great many Americans. In our thinking today we take women's suffrage for granted. For hundreds

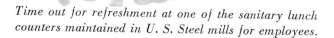

A change of shift at a steel mill — steelworkers driving in at the left and others walking from the main gate.

Time out for refreshment at one of the sanitary lunch counters maintained in U. S. Steel mills for employees.

71

of years it has been the traditional right of a man who founded a business to run it largely as he saw fit, hiring and firing employees, establishing hours and wages and other conditions of employment. It was perfectly natural for such men in their thinking to resist the idea of employees banding together in unions, instinctively fearing an invasion of what they considered to be their rights and prerogatives. The majority of employers were fair to their workers,

but some were ruthless and oppressive. As our industries expanded and individual companies often employed thousands of men, it was perfectly natural for employees to realize that "in numbers there is strength" and that unionization would put a powerful weapon in their hands in dealing with employers.

Here again there has been a revolution in thinking and the right of free men to form unions of their own choosing for the purpose of collective bargaining has been accepted to such an extent that it has been written into the law of the land.

It has also been expressed in the law of the land that responsibility should be commensurate with privilege and that justice requires that management and unions should be equally answerable for their actions affecting the public interest.

THE ALL-IMPORTANT QUESTION

So here we are at the half century mark, with Big Unions and Big Business, Small Unions and Small Business, operating under the private enterprise system which has progressively raised our living standards and can continue to raise them, as our productivity increases, if we do not tamper with basic principles. The question we must ask ourselves is whether our progress in *thinking*, in terms of getting along together, has kept pace with our progress in machines. In a word, have we matured sufficiently as human beings to be worthy of the modern miracles which science has given us?

The answer depends on the extent to which management and labor, putting public interest foremost, can maintain harmonious relations, based on a complete understanding of each other's rights, problems and responsibilities.

Heavy manual labor and crude machinery characterized the operation of a sheet mill early in this century.

A NEW LANDMARK IN THINKING

The rights and responsibilities of management and labor have been recognized and defined. What is needed now is a new kind of thinking which goes beyond the formal words of contracts. U. S. Steel and the United Steelworkers of America-C.I.O. recognized this in their 1947 contract, which declared that their common goal of friendly, cooperative relations depends less on words than on attitudes. What is an attitude but a way of thinking? The contract states: "Proper attitudes must be based on full understanding of and regard for the respective rights and responsibilities of both the Company and the Union." The contract goes on to say that such attitudes can best be encouraged when both parties "are sincerely concerned with the best interest and well-being of the business and all employees."

This is a landmark of enlightened thinking on management-labor relations. It means turning to a fresh page, where the writing should be inspired by mutual good will, trust and respect, free from recrimination and name-calling. It implies that prosperity is indivisible and that the well-being of one party cannot be jeopardized without detriment to the well-being of the other.

The men who direct the affairs of U. S. Steel earnestly hope and believe that the declared intention of the Corporation and the Union to place more emphasis on attitudes than on words—more stress on spirit than on substance—will take them nearer the goal of harmonious, cooperative relationships, for their mutual well-being and the well-being of the nation.

TRADITIONAL POLICY OF U. S. STEEL

This goal has long been the aim of U. S. Steel's traditional policy in relations with its employees. A good start toward this goal was given by the labor policies of Judge Elbert H. Gary, who was genuinely concerned with the working conditions, safety and adequate payment of U. S. Steel employees. Ida M. Tarbell, in her book, "The Life of Elbert H. Gary," published in 1925, wrote: "I do not believe that there is anything connected with the Corporation—finance, operation, expansion of foreign business—to which he gives more attention and from which he gets more pleasure than from the operation of these labor activities." The labor activities to which she referred were the various programs Judge

Gary had initiated for the betterment of working conditions. Miss Tarbell also wrote that from the year in which the Corporation was formed there were few weekly meetings of the executive body in which a part of the time was not given over to the consideration of some phase of the life and interests of the workers. "I have gone over many pages of the Corporation minutes," she observed, "and I cannot recall a single meeting in which some action was not taken showing that one phase or another of labor had been under consideration. Usually this action called for the voting of money."

TRAIL BLAZING IN LABOR RELATIONS

More than any single person, Judge Gary was responsible for the abolition of the twelve-hour day. This work period, incidentally, was not begun by employers in the steel industry, but was practically forced by the workers themselves in the 1880's and 1890's, over the opposition of employers who were insisting on an eight-hour day in the interest of greater production. The workers preferred the twelve-hour day for a number of reasons. They expected that the eight-hour shift would reduce their earnings and bring in so many more men that there would not be enough work to go around. Furthermore, the workmen, especially in the skilled trades, had adjusted their lives to the twelve-hour plan. They worked at a leisurely pace and there were periods in the day when a man had little or no work to do. Skilled men on the twelve-hour shifts were actually kept busy no more than two-thirds of the time. Unskilled twelve-hour men had their rest periods too, but they were less frequent than those of skilled employees.

The disadvantages of the twelve-hour day were

Safer, healthier working conditions and a high degree of mechanization are typical of today's rolling mills.

Judge Gary was responsible more than any other person for the abolition of the 12-hour day in the steel industry.

effect and had made some gains in that direction, World War I broke out. Under the pressure of demand for greater steel production the percentage of men working the longer shift in the Corporation's plants increased from 22 to 32 per cent.

"THE TWELVE-HOUR DAY MUST GO"

As soon as the war was over, one of Judge Gary's first acts regarding labor policy was to resume his advocacy of the eight-hour day, not only for U. S. Steel but for the entire iron and steel industry. "The twelve-hour day must go," became his battle cry. Finally, at the request of President Harding, Judge Gary took the matter up with the American Iron and Steel Institute, of which he was the acknowledged spokesman. As a result of his effort, companies representing 75 per cent of the iron and steel industry agreed to abolish the twelve-hour day at the earliest practical moment. Their pledge was kept. Herbert Hoover, then Secretary of Commerce, credited Judge Gary with having "made the largest possible contribution to the final solution of the twelve-hour day in the steel industry."

obvious. The worker was left few leisure hours to spend with his family, and in which to pursue healthful recreation and self-improvement. Opposition to the practice came first from outside the steel industry—from social workers, pastors, and other civic-minded citizens. It is true that by 1919 leaders of the steelworkers had begun to champion the eight-hour day and made it one of their demands in the strike of that year for union recognition.

In 1911, Judge Gary took the lead in advocating abolition of the twelve-hour day. However, a change in working schedules of such a fundamental nature could not be accomplished overnight. It was anticipated that the eight-hour day would increase production costs 15 per cent and require 60,000 more employees. While U. S. Steel was still working out a method to put the shorter day into

During the twenty-six years in which Judge Gary was the chief executive officer of U. S. Steel, he kept a firm hold on the direction of programs for the betterment of working conditions. Largely at his instigation, upwards of $150,000,000 was spent for these purposes. On numerous occasions, wages were raised voluntarily when he felt that business conditions of the Corporation justified it. Judge Gary had been the chief organizer of U. S. Steel. He had fathered it and seen it through its growing pains and believed he knew what was in the best interest of the employees and when wages could be raised and how much. His attitude was paternalistic, as was the attitude of many top executives of that period, but it happened that Judge Gary was a

kind and just man. He believed, as he once said, that no industry can permanently succeed that does not treat its employees equitably and humanely.

THE 1919 STRIKE

Progressive as were Judge Gary's ideas on management's responsibility toward employees, he belonged to the school whose thinking shied away from the need and right of employees to organize themselves into unions of their own choosing for the purpose of collective bargaining. He was open-minded about a company union which limited its members to the employees of a single employer, but was strongly opposed to a closed shop. In the strike of 1919, called for the purpose of organizing the steel industry, Judge Gary refused to see representatives of the strike committee on the grounds that they did not represent workers of the Corporation and had never been in its employ and therefore had no right

Benjamin Fairless and Philip Murray, Presidents of U. S. Steel and the C.I.O. sign their first union contract.

to speak for them. The chief leader in the organizing campaign was William Z. Foster, now general secretary of the American Communist Party, who formed the National Committee for Organizing Iron and Steel Workers, which called a strike throughout the steel industry in September 1919.

The strikers in some plants were persuaded that if the strike succeeded the workers would take over the management of the plant. It was reported that some of them had already portioned out the executive jobs among them. The movement did not represent the sentiment of the majority of the men and the strike was abandoned in January 1920.

Judge Gary had acted according to his convictions and the predominant thinking of that day. But thinking has changed a great deal since then. In 1937, U. S. Steel, under the Chairmanship of Myron

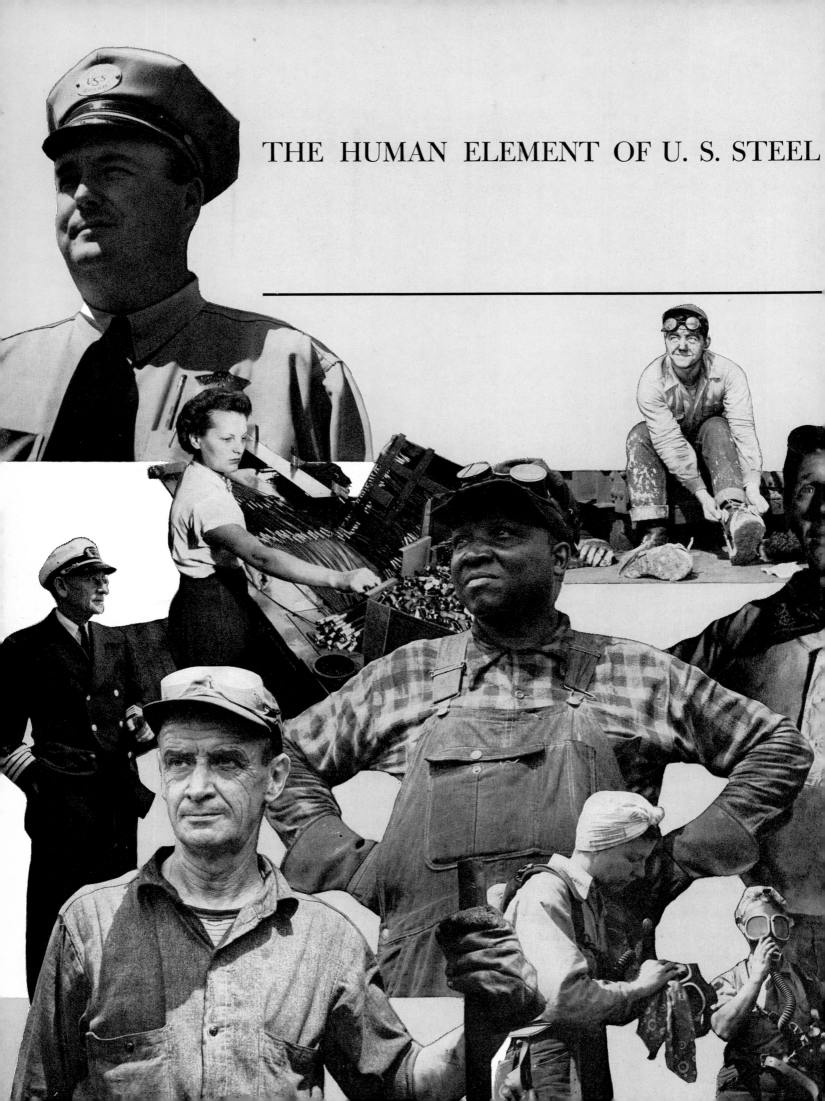

THE HUMAN ELEMENT OF U. S. STEEL

C. Taylor, voluntarily negotiated and signed a contract with the Steel Workers Organizing Committee, which, in May 1942, became the United Steelworkers of America, an affiliate of the Congress of Industrial Organizations, commonly called the C.I.O. Thus, U. S. Steel was the first to sign a company-wide contract with the union.

THE GROWTH OF
INDUSTRIAL RELATIONS

New concepts in the relationship between management and labor have brought new phrases into our language, such as "collective bargaining" and "industrial relations." At the beginning of this century, the point of contact between the employer and the workman for most purposes was the employment office. The employment officer hired the men and kept a record of their employment for payroll purposes. Otherwise, relations between management and the men in the mills were on an informal basis. If a man had a grievance, he took it to his foreman. Should he fail to obtain satisfaction there, he could walk into the "main office" of the superintendent of the mill and make his complaint known.

Long before the term "industrial relations" was a part of our vocabulary, U. S. Steel pioneered in this field. These activities were concerned with safe and sanitary working conditions, the administration of pension and compensation funds and other matters relating to the well-being of employees. They had become so varied and extensive by 1910 that a new department was created to coordinate and direct them—the Bureau of Safety, Sanitation and Welfare. The title indicates the limitation of its functions. The employment office still carried on its duties as before.

The growth of unionism, and particularly the negotiation of contracts between a company and a union, brought about the need of heading up all management-employee relationships in one office, which generally became known as the Industrial Relations Department. It meant far more than a new department with a new name. Industrial relations is a new, specialized function which has rapidly taken on the status of a profession. The director of industrial relations is a student in human relations. Over and above his supervision of personnel, training, safety and related matters, he is chiefly concerned with bringing about more harmonious relationships with employees, upon which the welfare of the country so much depends.

THE HANDLING OF GRIEVANCES

As in the past, any employee of U. S. Steel is assured of a fair hearing for any grievance he may wish to

make known. The 1947 contract and earlier contracts between the Corporation and the Union established a definite procedure for union members. A grievance may go through five successive steps, ending in a Board of Conciliation and Arbitration.

If an employee wishes to make a complaint against the management's administration of the contract, he simply tells it to his foreman, who is the first line of management. In the event the foreman's reply does not satisfy the employee, he may fill out a Grievance Form, which constitutes the first formal step. After discussing this Form with the plant superintendent, the foreman writes his reply.

Often the reply satisfies the employee. But if he and the Union still believe that a valid grievance exists, they may, if they wish, progress through

higher levels of management and union responsibility until the grievance reaches the fifth and final stage—the Board of Conciliation and Arbitration. The Board consists of one member from the Union, one from the Corporation and a third member, acting as the Chairman, representing neither and acceptable to both. The decision of the Board is final and binding on both parties. In every case where the grievance has reached the Board, its verdict has been accepted by the Corporation and the Union.

SAFETY

Since 1906, when U. S. Steel first began a safety program, the Corporation has played a leading role in the safety movement in this country, and in 1913 helped to form the National Safety Council.

The national slogan, "Safety First," may be traced back to Henry C. Frick. In 1890, when he was president of the H. C. Frick Coke Company, he issued a bulletin to all mine superintendents which said in part: "We shall always keep the fact prominently in our mind that it is the desire of our company, and our duty as well, that we make safety of the lives of our employees our first and foremost important business."

Nine years later Frick inaugurated the country's first industry-wide safety campaign, with the slogan, "Safety First, Quality Second, Cost Third." The H. C. Frick Coke Company was acquired by U. S. Steel when the Corporation was formed in 1901. In the ensuing years the Frick statement was adopted by various plants of the Corporation and shortened through usage to "Safety First," a phrase that was taken up by safety movements all over America.

In the early years of this century, Judge Gary had become disturbed by the number of accidents

Management and Union are represented at a Grievance Committee meeting to consider an employee's complaint.

By every feasible means U. S. Steel trains employees in safe working habits. Above, an on-the-job safety class.

Numerous safety signs, as well as training, have contributed to the outstanding safety records of U. S. Steel.

in the steel industry. He appointed a Safety Committee to study means of reducing the hazards of work. This Committee still exists as the U. S. Steel Safety Advisory Committee. In addressing a meeting of the original Committee in 1908, he summed up U. S. Steel's safety policy:

"I am in hearty sympathy with the movement. We should like to take a prominent part, a leading part, in any movement and in every movement that is practical to protect employees of the different corporations in which we are interested, and any requisition which is made for the expenditure of money to install equipment to protect our people will be honored."

Judge Gary at first believed that the chief cause of accidents was hazardous working conditions and improperly protected machinery, and that accidents could be drastically reduced or virtually eliminated by installing proper safeguards and protecting machinery. During the first eight years of the program, approximately $10,000,000 was spent in providing safeguards and in the correction of conditions responsible for accidents.

But accidents did not decline as much as Judge Gary anticipated. It was evident that the protection of machinery and the elimination of hazardous conditions would not of themselves prevent accidents and that not enough attention had been given to the human factor. A twofold program was pursued, to make the machines safer and to train the workers in safety habits. From then on the number of accidents declined rapidly, mostly as a result of safety training.

PLANTS ARE DESIGNED FOR SAFETY

By every possible means, year in and year out, the need for safe working habits is driven into the consciousness of the employees. It is easier to acquire safe working habits where the least dangers exist. For that reason, in the blueprint stage, U. S. Steel mills, mines and other facilities are designed for safety. Safety engineers give the same careful attention when an old piece of equipment is replaced by a new one.

Constant vigilance is also maintained to see that no dangerous conditions develop. Throughout U. S. Steel's operations, Supervisors of Safety make constant inspections of all physical facilities at work locations. If dangerous or defective conditions are found they are at once reported and corrected.

ACCIDENT RATE DROPS SHARPLY

A code is used by the National Safety Council to measure the frequency and severity rates of accidents. The frequency rate indicates the number of disabling accidents that occur for every million man-hours worked. If a plant worked one million

hours and had five disabling accidents, its frequency rate would be 5. The severity rate expresses the average number of days lost from work through accidents for every thousand man-hours worked.

The combined accident frequency rate for the operations of U. S. Steel was reduced 92 per cent between 1912 and 1950. In 1950, the steel manufacturing operations had an accident frequency rate of 2.67. This was 56 per cent lower than the rate for the steel industry, as computed by the U. S. Bureau of Labor Statistics.

Particular attention has been given to reducing the dangers of coal mining in the United States. Since 1940 the fatal accident frequency in the bituminous coal industry has been reduced 52 per cent and the non-fatal frequency 32 per cent. U. S. Steel's safety record is considerably better than the average of the industry. In 1950, the fatal accident frequency in U. S. Steel's bituminous coal mining was 65 per cent lower than the bituminous coal mining industry's, on a million man-hours basis. On the same basis, the Corporation's record in non-fatal

Plants are designed for safety. The worker operates at a safe distance from hot metal, protected by a screen.

accident frequency was 73 per cent lower than that of all bituminous coal companies.

There have been fewer severe accidents in all of U. S. Steel's operations over the years. The severity rate dropped 47 per cent between 1945 and 1950.

SAFETY RECORDS AND AWARDS

Employees of U. S. Steel subsidiaries are proud of their safety performances which have established numerous outstanding records and have won many awards for distinguished contributions to safety. In April 1947, the National Safety Council began a program of safety awards to industry. Since that time, subsidiary plants of U. S. Steel have won 48 Distinguished Service to Safety Awards, the top honor bestowed by the Council. A few safety records will be cited here.

According to National Safety Council records, the all-time safety record for the entire American steel industry was set by Ellwood Works of U. S. Steel's National Tube Company on February 13, 1951, when employees had worked 385 days for a total of 6,743,644 man-hours without a lost-time

U. S. Steel plant holds steel industry's safety record —6,743,644 man-hours without a lost-time accident.

accident. The previous record was 5,598,367 man-hours, established by the Colorado Fuel and Iron Corporation.

Another plant of National Tube Company—National Works—holds fourth place in all-time safety records of the steel industry. National Safety Council information credits employees of the plant in the winter of 1949-50 with a total of 4,949,404 continuous man-hours free of disabling injuries.

The world's record in the wire products division of the steel industry is held by the Joliet, Illinois, plant of the American Steel & Wire Company, where the employees worked slightly more than ten years, or a total of 6,442,278 man-hours, without a single disabling accident. The period extended from July 3, 1928 to July 18, 1938.

The Wilson-Snyder Manufacturing Division of the Oil Well Supply Company won the National Safety Council's first place award in the construction machinery industry in 1948 for having worked 2,850,000 man-hours since June 16, 1945, without a disabling injury. At the time the award was made, no accident had yet occurred and the plant continued its unblemished record until June 16, 1950, when it had accumulated 3,089,250 injury-free man-hours. This was exactly five years that the employees had worked continuously without an accident.

Four plants and their employees of the Universal Atlas Cement Company were awarded trophies by the Portland Cement Association for their safety achievement in having operated more than one year without a disabling injury. One of the plants at Northampton, Pa., did not have an accident while working 5,000,000 man-hours for more than five consecutive years. The other three plants are located at Hannibal, Mo., Waco, Texas, and Leeds, Ala.

The U. S. Bureau of Mines each year awards six Sentinels of Safety trophies to the mines and quarries with the best safety performances. U. S. Steel's mining operations have been prominent among the winners of these awards. The Bureau also holds an annual competition among various mining and quarrying groups. The winners receive a Certificate of Achievement in Safety. In 1950, U. S. Steel subsidiaries won eight of the certificates.

BIG PLANTS HAVE
LOWEST ACCIDENT RATE

At the President's Conference on Industrial Safety held in 1950, it was shown conclusively that the accident rate is lower in large companies than in small ones. The Committee on Accident Records, Analysis and Use reported to the Conference its conclusion that "the greatest accident-prevention problems exist in the smaller plants, specifically in those having fewer than 500 employees."

Two sets of data were submitted to the Conference, one prepared by the National Safety Council and the other by the U. S. Bureau of Labor Statistics. The National Safety Council found in its 1949 studies that the accident frequency rate in plants employing more than 500 persons was less than half that of plants with fewer than 500 employees. The severity rate was also appreciably lower.

A special study of three industries, made by the Bureau of Labor Statistics, showed that in general the accident rate declined as the number of employees per plant increased.

TRAINING FOR
TOMORROW'S LEADERS

In our competitive system, a product of the best quality, which gives the best service, and is sold at a

Employees have opportunities to train for various jobs to aid advancement. Here is a typical training class.

competitive price, is the one that the customer will prefer to buy. U. S. Steel believes that a well-trained employee turns out quality products. That is why in U. S. Steel subsidiaries, from mining the ore to making finished steel products, so much emphasis is placed on employee training.

The steel industry has been traditionally known for the large number of men who have risen through the ranks to top executive positions. U. S. Steel's various training programs and its promotion-from-within policy assure a constant supply of qualified and experienced men rising through the ranks to fill responsible positions as vacancies occur.

Training in U. S. Steel takes various forms. The training of a new, inexperienced employee is relatively simple, because he is generally started at a job that is easily and quickly learned. From then on, various classes afford him an opportunity to improve his skills and increase his value to the company and to himself.

TRADES APPRENTICESHIP

To maintain peak efficiency in steel operations, the furnaces, machines and tools must be kept in excellent repair at all times. Almost half as many employees are required in maintenance work as in actual production. The important function of maintenance is performed by journeymen, such as machinists, electricians, pipefitters, riggers, bricklayers and others. To train men for these jobs, U. S. Steel maintains a Trades Apprenticeship Program.

Each year a number of qualified men are accepted as apprentices. Upon successful completion of his apprenticeship, a graduate receives an engraved Certificate of Apprenticeship. From then on the limit of opportunity lies only within himself. Many of the

Apprentice training class for pattern makers, craftsmen who make the patterns for iron and steel castings.

Corporation's supervisors and executives have come up from the ranks of journeymen.

COLLEGE RECRUITING

Many paths of opportunity are offered to college and university graduates in U. S. Steel. The Industrial Relations Departments of subsidiary companies maintain contacts with institutions of higher learning for recruiting each year a number of graduates for training as future technicians and executives. Opportunities for development and advancement exist throughout all phases of U. S. Steel's operations, making it possible for the college recruit to progress to the ranks of management. These opportunities are equally shared by men who do not have a college education, but who possess the necessary aptitudes and abilities. U. S. Steel looks to its young men of today to assume leadership tomorrow in The Industrial Family That Serves the Nation.

FINDING A PLACE FOR VETERANS

During World War II, there were more than 113,000 stars in U. S. Steel's service flag. Long before victory was won, U. S. Steel made plans to employ returning veterans. Thousands of jobs were studied in relation to war disabilities. Based on these studies, a program was instituted for training physically handicapped veterans. Many severely wounded veterans, some of whom had suffered the loss of one or more limbs, were successfully rehabilitated and given responsible jobs. Two years after the end of the war, U. S. Steel had on its payroll 77,000 veterans, of whom 40,000 were former employees.

PRODUCTIVITY—
THE KEY TO PROGRESS

The phenomenal rise in American living standards

in the past fifty years has been made possible by a constant yearly increase in the productivity of our economic machine. Productivity is measured in different ways, but is most commonly spoken of in terms of "output per man-hour." While the skill of workmen and the efficiency of management have been improved greatly in this century, the spectacular increase in productivity has been due almost entirely to better machines—better "tools of production." This was acknowledged by the U. S. Bureau of Labor Statistics in its statement: "The long-term upward trend of output per man-hour is due mainly to technical improvements in industry."

The investment of hundreds of millions of dollars in improved tools of production has made it possible for the wages of American workers to advance more rapidly than the cost of living. Productivity is the golden key to progress, for only by enlarging the total stream of goods and services, while at the same time decreasing unit costs, can any of us—management, labor, farmers, profes-

86

sional men and women—realize any permanent gain.

MANY GAINS OF
U. S. STEEL EMPLOYEES

In the operation of the private enterprise system, in which the owners endeavor to obtain compensation for the tools which they provide, the principal beneficiaries have been the employees. They have benefited from a greater availability of jobs, created by investment in the tools of production. They have benefited in terms of lessened effort at work, shorter hours, increased safety at their jobs and most of all in real wages which enable them to obtain more and better goods from an hour's labor. These facts are well illustrated by the records of U. S. Steel.

Employees of U. S. Steel are among the highest paid in American industry. The average hourly earnings of $1.83 in 1950 were 37 cents an hour higher than the average hourly rates in all manufacturing industries. This 37 cents an hour difference was equal to approximately $210,000,000 of total wage and salary costs of U. S. Steel in 1950.

U. S. Steel's wage level is interesting in another respect. According to a study of half a dozen industries made by the U. S. Department of Labor, Big Business pays its workers from 25 to 40 per cent more per hour than Small Business.

A comparison of wages in the steel industry with those of other industries, based on the U. S. Bureau of Labor Statistics figures, shows that in December 1950, hourly earnings in the steel industry were higher than in other industry groups. Hourly wage rates were $1.83 in the steel industry, $1.61 in durable goods industries, $1.54 in all manufacturing industries and $1.44 in non-durable goods industries.

Since 1940, the increase in average weekly earnings of U. S. Steel employees has kept ahead of the rise in the cost of living. Taking 1940 as a base point of 100, the cost of living rose 78 points through December 31, 1950, while average weekly earnings mounted 135 points—a gain of 57 points.

Seen from another viewpoint, the average U. S. Steel employee in 1950 worked 31.1 hours less a week than in 1913, while the buying power of an hour's work in terms of the 1950 dollar, increased from 61 cents to $1.83, or nearly 200 per cent.

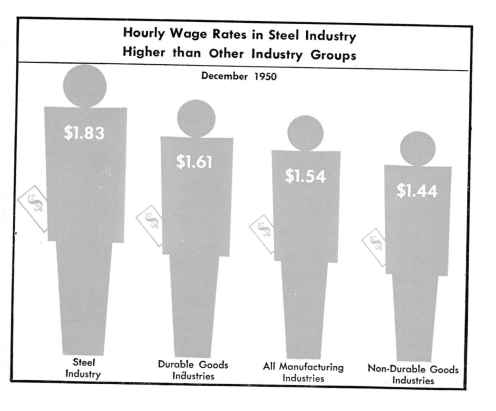

Hourly Wage Rates in Steel Industry Higher than Other Industry Groups

December 1950

Steel Industry	Durable Goods Industries	All Manufacturing Industries	Non-Durable Goods Industries
$1.83	$1.61	$1.54	$1.44

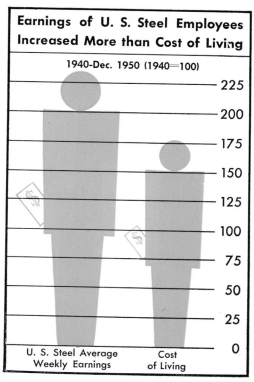

Earnings of U. S. Steel Employees Increased More than Cost of Living

1940-Dec. 1950 (1940=100)

225
200
175
150
125
100
75
50
25
0

U. S. Steel Average Weekly Earnings   Cost of Living

A FAIR DAY'S WORK— A FAIR DAY'S PAY

Fairness to all groups is the basis of democracy. But difficulty arises when what one group considers fair is considered unfair by another group. U. S. Steel seeks to be fair to its employees in the wages it pays but there has not always been agreement with the Union on what is a fair rate of pay for a given job, and a fair effort on the part of the worker. In fact, a study U. S. Steel made some years ago of employees' grievances showed that about 70 per cent were complaints concerning wages. There were thousands of separate jobs and thousands of rates of pay. Sometimes the complaint was settled satisfactorily within the plant, but often the grievance led to a work stoppage by one or more employees. The settlement of one grievance would give rise to sporadic grievances by others who felt that they deserved what the first had obtained.

Clearly the need was to agree on some means of standardizing jobs and pay rates. Beginning in 1940, an attempt was made in this direction but without much success. Then during World War II, the War Labor Board directed companies in the steel industry and the United Steelworkers of America-C.I.O. to negotiate the elimination of alleged wage rate inequities within plants by grouping all jobs within specific job classes and establishing wage rates for each job classification.

In 1945, U. S. Steel and the Steelworkers Union reached an agreement that an employee is entitled to a fair day's pay in return for which the Company is entitled to a fair day's work. To determine a fair day's pay U. S. Steel and the Union agreed on 32 job classifications and for each one a standard hourly wage rate. They further agreed that a fair day's work is the amount that can be produced by an employee working at a normal pace and effectively utilizing his time. A normal pace was defined as "equivalent to a man walking, without load, on smooth, level ground at a rate of three miles per hour."

When a man is working at a normal pace during all portions of the hour except that which is required for reasonable rest and personal needs, he is giving a "standard performance" and is entitled to the standard hourly wage rate for that job. If an employee works above the standard performance and is on an incentive basis, he receives extra pay at the rate of one per cent of his base pay for every one per cent that he exceeds the standard job performance.

Since this program was undertaken there have been fewer unauthorized work stoppages in the steel producing operations directly attributable to wage disputes. Two years before the agreement there were 396 work stoppages, 219 of which were caused by pay grievances. In 1945, work stoppages dropped to 216, of which 78 were due to wage difficulties. By 1948, work stoppages had dropped to 22, with only 7 attributable to wage disputes.

PENSIONS

U. S. Steel has long been an advocate of pensions for retired employees, and by the end of 1950 had paid $198,625,000 in pensions. On that date, 14,445 former employees were receiving pensions. The first old age pension plan was established on January 1, 1911, by the joint action of U. S. Steel and Andrew Carnegie, and was called the United States Steel and Carnegie Pension Fund. The fund of $12,000,000 consisted of $8,000,000 provided by U. S. Steel and the $4,000,000 Carnegie Relief Fund created by Andrew Carnegie in 1901. No contributions were required from employees.

On January 1, 1940, the pension plan was amended to provide that employees retiring with 25 or more years of continuous service would be eligible for pensions based on the number of years of such service prior to January 1, 1940.

On April 22, 1940, a supplemental pension plan was adopted providing pensions to the cost of which both U. S. Steel and participating employees contribute. Since the Social Security Act and the Railroad Retirement Act provide old age pensions for employees earning up to $3,000 and $3,600 a year respectively, the contributory plan provides that participating employees contribute on earnings in excess of those amounts. The plan provides upon retirement at 65, an annual life pension equivalent to one per cent of aggregate earnings upon which contributions have been made.

U. S. Steel's experience with pensions inclined it to favor the principle of contributory pensions. The largest pension system in the world, the Federal Social Security program, and a large majority of industrial group life insurance plans, including U. S. Steel's, are based on the American tradition that a man should contribute toward his pension and insurance benefits. However, after other steel companies in 1949 agreed to pay the entire cost of pensions, U. S. Steel signed agreements on similar terms with respect to its non-contributory pension plan, and continued in effect the principal provisions of its contributory plan.

THE NEW PENSION PLAN

The agreement provides minimum pensions of $100 a month, including old age Government benefits, to employees who retire at 65 with at least 25 years of continuous service. An employee may retire, under certain conditions, after 15 years of continuous service in which case his pension is calculated on a proportional basis.

The agreement also provides for an insurance plan, covering death, sickness, accident and hospitalization benefits to employees. The cost is to be five cents for each hour worked, to be shared equally by U. S. Steel and the employee.

SUPPLY STORES FOR EMPLOYEES

In 1873, two years after Henry C. Frick began to mine coal and manufacture beehive coke in western Pennsylvania, he became concerned with the inaccessibility of food and household stores to employees living at some distance from shopping centers. To make such necessities conveniently available to them at low cost he began to maintain stores in outlying districts. As the H. C. Frick Coke Company grew in size, the number of stores was increased.

After Frick became a partner of Andrew Carnegie in 1882, bringing his properties with him into the Carnegie Company, the store service to employees was continued. A year later the partners set up a separate organization to handle the stores and called it the Union Supply Company.

This company came with the Carnegie properties into the formation of U. S. Steel. Union Supply Company, as a U. S. Steel subsidiary, has continued and extended its service to employees. Organized originally for miners, the company now serves employees of other U. S. Steel subsidiaries and the public in outlying districts, through 105 stores in six states, with quality merchandise consisting chiefly of food, clothing and house furnishings.

U. S. STEEL A GOOD PLACE TO WORK

The men and women of U. S. Steel's industrial family are nearly 300,000 strong. They live and work in communities all over the nation, from the Atlantic to the Pacific Coasts and from northern Minnesota to southern Texas. They are Americans of many racial origins, good citizens, able, efficient and loyal workers. It is they who mine the raw materials, fabricate and erect steel, and man the ore vessels and railroads, operate the mills, perform the clerical and administrative work.

U. S. Steel's employees numbered 168,000 in the first year the Corporation started business. They found U. S. Steel a good place in which to work and so have others who joined the Corporation in succeeding years. In 1950, there were more than 49,000 employees who had over 25 years of service with U. S. Steel. On December 31, 1950, there were 277 pensioned employees with 50 years of service when they retired, having begun their careers with predecessor companies.

Working with U. S. Steel has become a tradition with many American families. Some employees are the third generation of the family to work with subsidiary companies. The Rushe family of Homestead, Pennsylvania, have amassed a total service record of more than 700 years.

There are thousands of father-and-son combinations and brother teams employed by U. S. Steel. Of the 10,000 male employees in the Homestead Works near Pittsburgh, more than 4,000 are father-and-son combinations. There are numerous teams of brothers working throughout U. S. Steel, ranging from two up to eight in a family.

The work of U. S. Steel requires many talents and many skills. In some instances these qualifications are best supplied by women. In offices, mills and other locations, the 16,000 women employees of U. S. Steel perform valuable and loyal service and constitute a very important asset of The Industrial Family That Serves the Nation.

Typical of many families working for U. S. Steel is the Streiner family, who have 94 years of continuous service.

Women employees in mills, offices, laboratories and other departments perform valuable work for U. S. Steel.

90

STEEL MAKING
IN AMERICA

WELCOME VISITORS

Basic
Facts

About

UNITED STATES STEEL

The Industrial Family That Serves the Nation

Annual Report
UNITED STATES STEEL

Business...Big and Small
...Built America

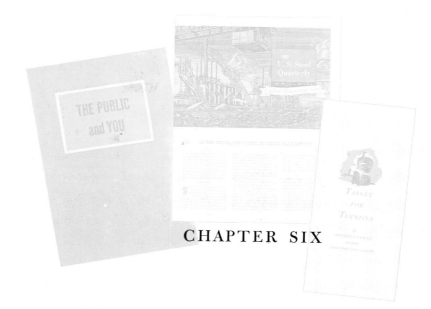

CHAPTER SIX

PUBLIC RELATIONS

United States Steel has to its credit a long list of "firsts" in various phases of steel manufacture, some of which are related elsewhere in this book. But U. S. Steel's pioneering activities were not restricted to the mines and the mills.

Long before the phrase "public relations" came into general use, Judge Elbert Gary introduced radical departures from customary business practice in the dissemination of information about U. S. Steel. It had been the tradition for most annual reports to contain a minimum of information, consisting chiefly of a bare financial statement with little or no elaboration. Judge Gary differed sharply from this concept of corporate responsibility to the public. He was firmly of the opinion that the officers of the Corpora-

Public Relations in action—Open House at a steel mill —Theatre Guild on the Air program, starring Anne Baxter and John Hodiak—press conference with Irving S. Olds—Two interested readers of an Annual Report.

tion should give a full and accurate account of their stewardship to the public and stockholders, in the belief that "the surest and wisest of all regulations is public opinion."

Thus, when it came time to issue U. S. Steel's first annual report in 1902, Judge Gary decided that it should give all the facts about the year's operations. Judge Gary's precedent was soon widely followed by other corporations. He also believed that stockholders were entitled to interim reports and he accordingly inaugurated the custom of issuing quarterly financial statements which were mailed to stockholders and released to the press.

NEW CONCEPTS IN PUBLIC RELATIONS

U. S. Steel has carried on the public relations policies initiated by Judge Gary. In the intervening years, public relations has become a highly developed profession of its own. Shortly after World War I when the term became part of our business and social vocabulary, "public relations" was synonymous with "publicity." It consisted chiefly of an attempt to obtain favorable notices in the press. A new attitude toward public relations developed in the late 1930's. It was realized more and more that good public relations begins with sound policies.

Keeping in step with this trend, U. S. Steel set up a separate department in 1936 to handle its public relations activities. Under the bylaws of the Corporation, the Chairman of the Board has general charge and supervision of public relations. As defined by the present Chairman, Irving S. Olds, "Public Relations is the creation and carrying out of broad policies which will be reflected in favorable public

opinion." This attitude is further explained by J. Carlisle MacDonald, who, as Assistant to Chairman, is charged with the responsibility of executing public relations policies: "It is, of course, desirable to use every possible medium to tell our story to the public. But it is far more important that we have a good story to tell. Management decisions are all-important. If the policies of a corporation are contrary to the interest of the nation—if its operating department is not meeting its production schedules or is delivering an inferior product—or the handling of its financial affairs is unsound—no amount of publicity material can build good public relations for that organization."

People all over America have seen how steel is made by watching one of U. S. Steel's numerous motion pictures.

DISTRICT PUBLIC RELATIONS OFFICES

Soon after U. S. Steel established a public relations department in 1936, it was realized that these two functions could not be performed solely from an executive office in New York. In order to decentralize the work, district public relations offices were organized in leading operating centers. Today these district offices are located in Birmingham, Boston, Chicago, Cleveland, Dallas, Duluth, Los Angeles, Pittsburgh, St. Paul, Salt Lake City, San Francisco, Washington and Worcester. The personnel of these offices are a part of their communities. They are well-informed on local happenings and are active in civic and commercial affairs of their cities. Through them, the Board of Directors and Corporation officials are kept advised of district developments which may have a bearing on the broad national policies of the Corporation. The district public relations directors are also in a position to keep their own communities informed regarding U. S. Steel, its products, policies and employees.

The public relations staff of U. S. Steel is relatively small, but in a real sense, the Corporation has thousands of public relations representatives. Each member of the managerial team is such a representative, and what he says and does can influence the public attitude toward U. S. Steel.

Benjamin F. Fairless, President, and other U. S. Steel officials give public talks on important developments.

MOTION PICTURES

Large numbers of people in all parts of the country who live many miles from a steel manufacturing center have been taken on an imaginary trip through a mill by watching one of U. S. Steel's numerous films. After producing several silent films, U. S. Steel in 1935 produced the first technicolor industrial film ever made. Called "Steel—Man's Servant," this vivid dramatic film of U. S. Steel's furnaces and mills has been seen by millions of people throughout the world. U. S. Steel's library contains many more films about specific Corporation activities. One of the latest, "Building for the Nations," released in 1950, portrays, step by step, erection of the steel framework for the United Nation's Secretariat Building in New York.

OTHER PUBLIC RELATIONS ACTIVITIES

Many other media are employed to acquaint the public with facts about U. S. Steel. Current and future plans are reported in releases to the press, radio and magazines. Public addresses by top Corporation officers are often published in booklet form and given wide distribution. Every three months, "The U. S. Steel Quarterly" brings timely news and facts about the Corporation to stockholders, press representatives and business, professional and educational leaders. Printed material includes a variety of educational and informative publications, ranging from a non-technical book, "Steel Making in America," to pamphlets describing research activities, new plants and products. For internal distribution, a booklet, "The Public and You" is designed to acquaint the management team with its part in public relations.

In plant communities U. S. Steel often holds

Open House in its mills to give its neighbors an opportunity to see firsthand how steel is made. Hundreds of thousands of people have seen the various plants of U. S. Steel at these Open House programs. As many as 30,000 visitors have gone through a plant in a single day.

THE THEATRE GUILD ON THE AIR

In 1945, U. S. Steel launched its first radio program, "The Theatre Guild on the Air." The objective, as stated by Mr. Olds, was "to bring to the public mind a better understanding of the affairs and poli-

cies of United States Steel, and to increase the appreciation of the part played by U. S. Steel and its subsidiary members in the nation's economy."

Every Sunday evening, from September to the early part of June, the program brings into millions of homes an hour-long dramatization of some of the finest plays, past and present, performed by the most distinguished stars of stage, screen and radio. Since its inception, "The Theatre Guild on the Air" has won more awards than any other radio program, and is required listening for many college and high school groups.

As a companion piece to entertain its listeners during the summer season, U. S. Steel in 1949 began a presentation of the NBC Symphony Orchestra, under the baton of celebrated conductors and featuring brilliant guest artists from the concert world and opera.

Brief, interesting messages, delivered at each broadcast, inform the public of the aims, operations and accomplishments of the Industrial Family that Serves the Nation—United States Steel.

U. S. Steel's radio program brings top flight dramatic entertainment into millions of homes Sunday evening.

Irving S. Olds receives the National Council of English Teachers' Award to U. S. Steel's Theatre Guild program.

Iron Ore

Limestone

Coal

PART TWO
CHAPTER SEVEN

RAW MATERIALS FOR IRON AND STEEL

From Minnesota, Wisconsin and Michigan, the United States has obtained most of the basic raw material for its fabulous industrial development and for waging two World Wars. That basic material was iron ore and represented roughly 85 per cent of all the iron ore mined in America during the present century.

Most of the ore was of a high grade, averaging more than 50 per cent iron, and was in a form that could be shipped directly from the mines to the steel mills. Up to the beginning of 1950, almost two and three-quarter billion gross tons of these "direct-shipping" ores had been mined in the Lake Superior region. Substantial reserves of the high grade,

Ore vessel alongside raw materials storage yard, with blast furnaces in background, South Works, Chicago.

direct-shipping ores still remain. Yet, when one considers that nearly half a billion tons of ore were required in World War II, it is evident that a sound program of conservation must be followed and other sources of ore developed to assure the future welfare and security of this nation.

PRIVATE INDUSTRY LOOKS AHEAD

Foreseeing the eventual depletion of the high grade ores in the Lake Superior region, private industry began many years ago to concern itself with the problem of obtaining iron ore from other sources. Plans and developments under way will assure this country all the iron ore it will need for an indefinite period. U. S. Steel alone plans to develop in the next twenty years an annual ore output of 25,000,000 gross tons *from sources not now being used.* The bulk of America's iron ore in the future will come from two sources—low grade iron ore reserves in the United States and from foreign mines.

NO SHORTAGE OF IRON ORE

Actually, there is no shortage of iron ore in America. Ores in abundant amounts, of varying qualities, exist elsewhere in the United States than the Lake Superior region. Substantial reserves are scattered through the Appalachian area, notably in New York, New Jersey, eastern Pennsylvania and Alabama. Iron ore deposits exist in several western states, predominantly in Utah, Wyoming and California.

Over the years, the emphasis will shift from one ore region to another, or from one particular kind of ore to another, in accordance with technical improvements and the needs of a dynamic, growing steel industry. From the Colonial period up to the middle of the nineteenth century, the relatively small needs of the iron industry were easily met from nearby ore deposits in the Eastern states. The introduction of modern steelmaking processes—the Bessemer converter and the open hearth furnace—coincided approximately with the discovery and development of the large, high grade ore reserves in the Lake Superior region. The vast expansion of the steel industry in the northeastern section of the United States during the past 90 years was made possible in a large measure by the accessibility of Lake Superior ores, which thereby gained a dominant position.

In recent years, increasing attention has been given to low grade ores in New York, New Jersey and eastern Pennsylvania. By "beneficiating" these ores, that is, removing waste matter and thereby raising the per cent of the iron content, the ores in those three states are assuming a stronger competitive position in the steel industry.

In Alabama, reserves are of a lower grade than the direct-shipping ores of Lake Superior, but the Alabama ores have persistently held their own, due in part to their unique chemical composition, but mostly to their proximity to Southern steel operations.

BILLIONS OF TONS OF LOW GRADE ORES

With the gradual depletion of high grade, direct-shipping iron ores in the Lake Superior region, it is anticipated that greater emphasis will be placed on the beneficiation of lower grades which great technical advances have made possible.

Interest now is centered chiefly in the low grade ores of the Lake Superior region, of which billions of tons exist, sufficient to last hundreds of years. Over forty years ago U. S. Steel began to study means of preparing some of these low grade ores into a usable form for the blast furnace. After some years of experimentation, U. S. Steel built a beneficiation plant in Minnesota in 1910, which has been improved from time to time and is still in use. Additional beneficiation plants were put into operation by other companies. Beneficiated ores today constitute about 25 per cent of the total ores shipped from the Lake Superior region.

CHIEF INTEREST IN TACONITE

There are various kinds of low grade ores. Those treated on a commercial scale up to 1950 consisted of the so-called "wash ores" and were a relatively minor source of supply. The technical problems encountered in improving wash ores were solved without too much difficulty. The particular low grade ore which is presently of the greatest interest and which exists in billions of tons is a hard rock called *taconite*, containing 25 to 30 per cent iron.

The conversion of taconite into an economical, usable form on a commercial scale has confronted the mining companies with formidable problems, both technical and financial. Through intensive research the technical problems are being mastered. U. S. Steel's work in this direction has been carried on by a subsidiary, Oliver Iron Mining Company, whose efforts were intensified in 1945 with the opening of a new research laboratory in Duluth. Much progress has been made and a plant is now being built, capable of turning out annually 500,000 gross tons of taconite concentrates with 60 per cent iron content. Based on the experience at this plant, Oliver Iron Mining Company will construct other and larger plants, as demand may require.

The equipment needed to treat taconite will be extensive and call for the investment of hundreds of millions of dollars by all the companies concerned. Beneficiation of taconite will incur substantial operating costs, which will be compensated in part by certain advantages. Compared to untreated direct-shipping ores of today, the higher iron content of the taconite concentrates will make possible a reduction in transportation costs. The higher iron content, combined with physical properties of the taconite product, is also expected to result in some economies in the operation of the blast furnace.

In sum, there is no scarcity of iron ore in the United States. The immediate task ahead is one of adjustment to other sources of supply. Utilization of the low grade ores is primarily a technological and financial problem.

IRON ORE OUTSIDE THE UNITED STATES

In their long-range planning, steel companies have also looked for iron ore sources outside the United States. Some companies intend to ship ore from Liberia. Another promising source has been dis-

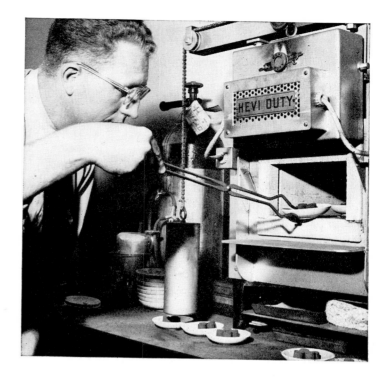

Research in taconite promises to make billions of tons of low grade iron ores available to the steel industry.

Big step in ore conservation—constructing a pilot plant for conversion of taconite for use in the blast furnace.

covered recently in the wild waste lands bordering Labrador and Quebec. Estimates place the deposits there at 400,000,000 gross tons of high grade direct-shipping open pit ore. Profitable mining of the Labrador ore will require the construction of a 370-mile railroad to a St. Lawrence River port. A number of companies have obtained mining concessions in Labrador. U. S. Steel is not among them.

CERRO BOLIVAR— U. S. STEEL'S MOMENTOUS DISCOVERY

In the interest of assuring an adequate iron ore supply for its furnaces and in the interest of conservation, U. S. Steel has pursued a twofold program for many years. One has been the beneficiation of domestic low grade ores and the other has been a search for large rich deposits elsewhere in North or South America. Numerous potential sources had become known to the Corporation, but none of them met the necessary requirements to justify full-scale development over a long period. In 1945, U. S. Steel undertook another search within the periphery of North and South America.

Toward the end of 1946, it looked as if the goal might not be achieved. Then one of the exploration teams in Venezuela conceived the idea of aerially photographing a certain region south of the Orinoco River. Geologists who studied the photographs became interested in a range of mountains about 70 miles south of the Orinoco River, and a field crew was dispatched to inspect it. They found large exposures of rich iron ore in several mountains. When the magnetometer recorded the highest responses ever shown anywhere in the world, the explorers had reason to believe that they had discovered a mass of iron ore of considerable depth and covering an extensive area. Samples of the ore ran as high as 60 per cent iron.

LARGE PROVEN DEPOSITS

Drillings at one of the mountains, La Parida, justified their expectations. In 1948, it was renamed Cerro Bolivar. Altogether, U. S. Steel has obtained concessions to high grade ore deposits, proven by drilling

to contain about 400,000,000 gross tons.

To develop and operate the Venezuelan mines, U. S. Steel formed a new subsidiary, the Orinoco Mining Company. A fleet of seagoing ore vessels will be required to bring the ore to seaports of the United States.

THE FUTURE IRON ORE SITUATION

Looking ahead into the 1960's, the iron ore situation in the industrial area east of the Mississippi River, where more than 80 per cent of the nation's steel is produced, may develop something like this:

Venezuelan ore will feed U. S. Steel's new mill on the Delaware River near Morrisville, Pennsylvania. It is also hoped that cost factors will develop favorably so that Venezuelan ore will be able to compete successfully in the much larger ore markets in Pittsburgh and as far west as Youngstown, Ohio, in sup-

Test drillings at Cerro Bolivar proved the existence of about 400 million tons of ore in U. S. Steel concessions.

Map below shows relative location of Venezuelan ore fields and steel producing centers in United States.

Cerro Bolivar, mountain of high grade iron ore deposits, discovered in Venezuela in 1946 by U. S. Steel.

plying not only U. S. Steel's plants but also outside companies who may wish to purchase it.

Venezuelan ore may also supplement ores now being mined for steel mills near Birmingham, Alabama, including U. S. Steel's subsidiary, Tennessee Coal, Iron and Railroad Company.

Taconite concentrates from the Lake Superior region will be used most economically in the steel mills of Chicago and Gary and other plants on or near Lake Michigan, and perhaps as far east as Youngstown and Pittsburgh. Thus, the Pittsburgh-

Youngstown area may be the commercial meeting point of Lake Superior taconites and Labrador, Venezuelan and other foreign ores. All these combined sources may be expected to assure an abundant supply of iron ore to the heart of America's competitive steel industry for many years to come.

U. S. STEEL'S ORE MINING OPERATIONS

Iron ore is presently mined by three U. S. Steel subsidiaries: Oliver Iron Mining Company, which carries on all the Corporation's operations in the Lake Superior region; Tennessee Coal, Iron and Railroad Company, which obtains ore from mines located near its steel plants outside Birmingham; and Columbia Iron Mining Company, which mines iron ore in Utah for U. S. Steel's steelmaking operations in the West. The Orinoco Mining Company is expected to begin mining iron ore in Venezuela within the next three to five years.

PROGRESS IN IRON ORE MINING

To feed the hungry blast furnaces of America has required the mining, handling, transporting and stor-

ing of mammoth quantities of iron ore each year. In some instances, the ore must be transported nearly 1,000 miles. Since transportation costs are significant factors in the cost of making steel, the efficient production and transportation of raw materials are of paramount importance.

Without doubt, constantly improved efficiency in mining and transporting iron ore is one of the reasons why low cost steel has been available to build America. U. S. Steel's three subsidiaries actively engaged in iron ore mining have had a prominent share in the many innovations which have made these achievements possible, particularly the two older companies which operate in the Lake Superior region and near Birmingham, Alabama.

OPEN PIT AND UNDERGROUND MINING

About 60 per cent of all the ore mined in America is produced in the open pit mines of the Lake Superior states. In these operations, the ore is simply scooped from the earth. From hand shovels and

Modern plant for conditioning iron ores for U. S. Steel's steelmaking operations near Birmingham, Alabama.

wooden horse-drawn cars of about one ton capacity, open pit iron ore mining has progressed to giant electric shovels capable of gouging out 14 tons of ore in one huge bite and dumping it into 50- to 70-ton capacity railway cars, hauled up the steep slopes of the mines by powerful Diesel locomotives.

Up to the end of World War II, trucks of 15-ton capacity were in general use in open pit mines. They have increased in size, and trucks up to 30-ton capacity are now used, with experiments being made with 40-ton models. By hauling ore from open pit mines too steep for locomotives, trucks have made large quantities of ore available that could not otherwise have been mined except by more costly underground methods.

Some underground iron ore mining is done in the Lake Superior region. The method is used entirely in Alabama. Progress in underground mining has been equally as marked as in open pit operations. It has been featured largely by increased mechanization and improvements in safety measures.

Ore cars have become larger, trains longer and locomotives more powerful. Advantage has been taken of Cor-Ten, the low alloy, high strength steel developed by U. S. Steel, which has made it possible to reduce the weight of railway cars substantially, thereby increasing their carrying capacity.

LOADING AND UNLOADING DOCKS

Loading docks at the head of the Lakes and unloading docks at the lower Lake ports have quickened the

Left, open pit mining in Lake Superior region. This method produces 60 per cent of ore mined in America.

Electric shovels scoop 14 tons of iron ore in open pit mining and dump them into railroad cars or trucks.

pace of operations. In 1905, it took 21 hours to fill an ore vessel and 33 hours to unload it. Now the time for both has been reduced to four or five hours, depending on the size of the vessel.

GREAT LAKES ORE VESSELS

The ore vessels on the Great Lakes constitute the largest inland fleet in the world. They serve as a vital waterway link between the ore fields and the steel-producing cities. Since part of the route is

Since 1901, vessels owned and chartered by the company have transported well over one billion tons of iron ore. In an average season the company's 61 vessels will travel three and a half million miles and transport 23,000,000 gross tons of ore, and 4,000,000 tons of coal and limestone.

From the early years to the present, the history of the Pittsburgh Steamship Company is one of continuous improvement in the design and propulsion machinery of the vessels to haul greater tonnages of ore more efficiently, economically and safely.

frozen in winter, the task of the ore vessels is to bring down some 85,000,000 gross tons of ore during the shipping season, from early spring to late fall, to keep the blast furnaces working all year round.

The Pittsburgh Steamship Company, U. S. Steel's ore-carrying subsidiary, has played a prominent and colorful role in the history of ore transportation on the Great Lakes during the Corporation's lifetime.

Manufacture of quality steel begins in the ore fields. Samples are collected from each ore car for analysis.

Laboratory tests of iron ore samples determine the grade of ore in each vessel load shipped to the steel mills.

One of U. S. Steel's ore vessels brings another load down the Great Lakes—this time to the Gary Works.

FIRST 600-FOOT ORE VESSELS

In 1906, the company put the first 600-foot ore vessels on the Great Lakes. Up to 1951, the company's largest vessels were 640 feet long, with a normal carrying capacity of 17,000 gross tons of ore. The average time for a round trip of the company vessels is six and a half days.

More ore will move faster down the Lakes in the three new vessels to be added to the Pittsburgh Steamship Company's fleet in time for the 1952 season. The new carriers will add 2,200,000 gross tons of ore to the fleet's yearly capacity. They will be 647 feet long and capable of holding 19,600 gross tons of ore. Their speed of 16 miles an hour with full load will permit a round trip in a little over five days.

COAL FOR THE COKE OVENS

Coal is another major raw material used by the steel industry. A special kind of bituminous coal, known as metallurgical or coking coal, is needed. In coke ovens, the coal is converted into coke, which serves in the blast furnace to smelt iron from iron ore.

One of the chief problems in relation to coking coal has been brought on by the mechanization of coal mining. When coal was mined by hand, the miner could remove slate, rock and other undesirable material. The mechanical coal loader gobbles up everything placed before it. This necessitated the construction of extensive plants for the sorting and cleaning of coal.

UNITED STATES STEEL COMPANY

U. S. Steel's coking coal is mined in three regions. Deposits near Birmingham, Alabama, are mined by the Tennessee Coal, Iron and Railroad Company for its steelmaking operations in that area. In the West, Geneva Steel Company, near Salt Lake City, Utah,

obtains its coal from extensive deposits existing within that state. Approximately 80 per cent of the coal mined by U. S. Steel is consumed in the Pittsburgh and Chicago districts and other plants in the northeastern section of the United States and comes principally from reserves in Pennsylvania, West Virginia and Kentucky. The 23 mines in those three states are operated by the United States Steel Company, which, as noted on page 45, was formed on January 1, 1951, by combining four subsidiaries, including H. C. Frick Coke Company and United States Coal and Coke Company. Since this book reviews the activities and accomplishments of U. S.

All aboard for the coal mine. Steel cars take the men down into a U. S. Steel coal mine near Geneva, Utah.

Machinery has replaced the coal miner's pick and mule —a mechanical loader in a mine near Birmingham, Ala.

Steel and subsidiary companies from 1901 to 1951, the operations of H. C. Frick Coke Company and United States Coal and Coke Company are discussed in this chapter, covering the period in which they were separate subsidiaries.

H. C. FRICK COKE COMPANY

In 1882, Henry Clay Frick, who had developed extensive coal mines and beehive coke ovens in western Pennsylvania, joined forces with his best customer, Andrew Carnegie. The coal and coke properties of both men were consolidated in the H. C. Frick Coke Company to supply coal and coke to the thriving iron foundries and blast furnaces of western Pennsylvania. Their joint properties came into U. S. Steel Corporation when it was formed in 1901.

The coal mines formerly operated by H. C. Frick Coke Company are located within 60 miles of Pittsburgh and serve the needs of U. S. Steel in that area. Of the 55,000 tons mined daily, the major portion goes in flat barges down the Monongahela River to Clairton, where it is converted into coke in by-product coke ovens.

In the past half century the Frick Company has mined over 700,000,000 tons of coal, with enough reserves to last well into the next century. In 1950, the company announced plans to open a new mine of 4,000 tons daily capacity and to reopen a closed mine of the same capacity in order to help meet the demands for coal required to produce more steel for the national defense program.

ROBENA MINE

Sharply increased demands for coking coal during

World War II caused a heavy drain on the developed reserves of the Frick Company. This necessitated the development of new sources of supply. One of the steps taken by the Frick Company to augment coal production was to complete development of the Robena Mine on the Monongahela River, 45 miles in a direct line south of Pittsburgh. The mine had first been opened in 1937, but preparatory work proceeded at a measured pace until the war, when plans were speeded up to bring it into production.

The Robena Mine near Pittsburgh is completely mechanized—one of the features is a 5-mile conveyor belt.

Robena Mine's coal washing plant, left, removes foreign matter and improves quality of coal for coke ovens.

Down the Monongahela River the coal goes in barges to U. S. Steel's by-product coke plant at Clairton, Pa.

112

Robena Mine embodies the last word in engineering and safety measures. Operations are completely mechanized. The mine has a daily production of 16,000 tons of washed coal. It is planned eventually to increase the daily output to 20,000 tons.

The relatively high sulphur content of the Robena reserves and mechanization of operations posed special problems. New methods had to be applied in the mine's washing plant to remove slate, rock and pyritic sulphur from the coal. The successful solution

of this difficult problem has made available additional extensive reserves of coking coal for U. S. Steel in its Pittsburgh operations.

UNITED STATES COAL AND COKE COMPANY

The United States Coal and Coke Company was

formed in 1902 and took over coal properties in southern West Virginia, brought into U. S. Steel by the Illinois Steel Company, one of the founding members of the Corporation. In World War I, the U. S. Coal and Coke Company acquired coal lands in southeastern Kentucky and since then has added to its properties.

The mines operated by this former subsidiary furnish coal to U. S. Steel mills in the Chicago district and elsewhere in the Great Lakes area. The problems met in refining the company's coal for the coke ovens were different from those met in some of the Frick mines, but they were no less difficult. The plant for cleaning and blending coal from the mine at Gary, West Virginia, is an engineering masterpiece. It was so designed and located that it can handle 25,000 tons of coal a day from seven mines.

KEEPING IN STEP WITH PROGRESS

In their coal mining operations, U. S. Steel subsidiaries have kept abreast of the tremendous advances made in the mining of coal and its preparation for the market during this century. Step by step, from the early 1900's, mechanization has progressed in the mines, replacing the miner's pick and mule. The old song, "My Sweetheart's a Mule in the Mine," is sung now only by reminiscing old-timers. Electricity has superseded steam power. Electric drills bore into the coal seams, and electric-powered coal-cutting machines cut deep into several sides of the block of coal to be shot down. In most mines, mechanical loaders gather up the loosened coal. Electric locomotives draw the steel mine cars. In one of the U. S. Steel mines near Pittsburgh, an underground conveyor belt more than five miles long takes coal from the mine to loading points on the Monongahela River.

Tennessee Coal, Iron and Railroad Company, as

long ago as 1892, installed the first coal washing plant in America, now a standard practice in the coal mining industry. In 1922, the company was the first in the nation to equip coal-cutting machines with a water spray line running through the cutter bar to prevent the accumulation of coal dust. This innovation has also since been adopted throughout the coal mining industry.

MINES ARE MUCH SAFER

Equally as great as technological progress in coal mining has been the advance in safety measures. Improved ventilation, steel beams to support the roofs of shafts, water spraying to reduce the accumulation of coal dust and other precautionary features, have greatly reduced the hazards of mining in U. S. Steel's coal mining operations. The result has been that U. S. Steel's safety record is considerably better than the average for the bituminous coal industry, as cited on pages 81 and 82.

New and improved coal mining equipment is constantly undergoing experimentation. For many years, coal mining companies have dreamed of a continuous mining machine—one that would combine all mining functions into one operation and permit an uninterrupted flow of coal from the mine face to the surface. In several of its mines, U. S. Steel is experimenting with various types of continuous mining machines. The results so far are encouraging.

LIMESTONE

The third important raw material used in making iron and steel is limestone. It serves as a refuse carrier, or flux, to combine with and take away impurities liberated in the blast furnace in the manufacture of iron, and in the conversion of iron into steel.

Limestone for U. S. Steel's operations in the Pittsburgh and Youngstown, Ohio, districts comes from the quarries and mines located in West Virginia and in western Pennsylvania. A large quarry at Calcite, Michigan, on Lake Huron, supplies limestone to U. S. Steel's operations in the Chicago district and elsewhere near the Great Lakes. Until January 2, 1951, the eastern operations were conducted by a subsidiary, Pittsburgh Limestone Corporation. On that date, the company was joined with another subsidiary, Michigan Limestone & Chemical Company, which operates the Michigan quarries. Limestone is obtained locally for subsidiary operations in the South and West.

In addition to supplying limestone for iron and steelmaking furnaces, the Michigan Limestone & Chemical Company produces stone for the chemical and cement industries and also for agricultural and other purposes.

Some limestone is mined underground, as in this Pennsylvania mine, but most of it is quarried in Michigan.

Self-unloader freighters at processing plant and storage yards of the limestone quarry, Calcite, Michigan.

Progress in the quarrying and mining of limestone has been similar to that made in the mining of iron ore and coal, and has been featured by increased mechanization and by equipment of greater capacity and faster action.

LIMESTONE FREIGHTERS

Expansion of limestone quarries in the upper Great Lakes region brought about the need for a special type of freighter to transport the stone to various points of use. At those points where the volume of cargo was large enough to require extensive unloading equipment at the docks, no problem was involved. At numerous points, however, the amount of stone handled was not sufficient to justify the installation of unloading facilities. To take care of customers at such points, Michigan Limestone & Chemical Company developed the self-unloader type of lake freighter. The self-unloader is equipped with belt conveyors which deliver the cargo from booms swung over the dock.

The development of the self-unloader vessel led to the formation of the Bradley Transportation Company, a U. S. Steel subsidiary, which operates a fleet of six of these vessels, chiefly to carry limestone from Calcite to lower Great Lakes ports. A seventh vessel, capable of carrying approximately 20,000 gross tons of limestone at 16 miles per hour, and discharging 4,000 gross tons per hour, is under construction.

CHAPTER EIGHT

MAKING IRON AND STEEL

The blast furnaces which smelt iron ore into iron and the steelmaking furnaces which, in turn, convert the iron into steel, constitute the heart of the steel industry. The industry has come a long way from the furnaces of 1900 to those of today which pour out molten rivers of iron and steel for the sinews of industrial America. A visitor to an open hearth furnace department of a steel mill grasps as perhaps in no other manner the industrial might of the United States, as he views the massive equipment functioning smoothly and the white-hot steel gushing forth when the furnace is tapped. The spectacle is grandiose and awesome.

The essential principles of iron and steel manufacture are the same today as they were when iron and steel first were made. Intense heat is applied to materials within a furnace, producing chemical and metallurgical changes. In the case of the blast furnace, coke is used as the fuel to "reduce" the iron ore to molten iron. The steelmaking furnaces are of three kinds—the Bessemer converter, the open hearth furnace and the electric furnace. U. S. Steel has the proud distinction of having taken part through present or predecessor companies in the first commercial operations in America of the three steelmaking furnaces.

GREAT PROGRESS IN THE FURNACES

The greatest progress in the steel industry during the past half century has been achieved in the steelmaking furnaces. These advances have been numerous and many of them have been of the greatest importance. A description of some of the most significant advances would involve technical explanations beyond the scope of this book. They may be summed

Ingot molds are filled with freshly-tapped molten steel from one of U. S. Steel's 313 open hearth furnaces.

up by saying that the principal improvements have been larger and more efficient furnaces, increased mechanization, and a vastly greater control of the operations. The last-named factor is of paramount importance in steelmaking furnaces for the manufacture of the metal to precise specifications to meet the exacting needs of today. These improvements relate to the structure, auxiliary equipment and the operation of the furnaces. Of equal importance has been the progress in the science of metallurgy.

When the modern Age of Steel began in the last century men were glad enough to make a product called steel in tons instead of pounds, and manufacturers were equally glad to buy it. For practical purposes, there was just one kind of steel. Men had learned by trial and error that steel could be modified by adding certain elements, but there was no real scientific basis to these practices. The first chemist employed by the iron and steel industry was hired by Andrew Carnegie's company in 1873. Chemists opened the eyes of steelmakers and the purchasers of steel by demonstrating that chemical analysis could serve as a guide in selecting the composition of steel required for specific uses.

Over the years, the chemist and the metallurgist

By-product coke plant at Clairton, Pa., producer of coke for U. S. Steel operations in the Pittsburgh area.

have come into their own. The quality of steel can now be precisely controlled by making it according to thousands of specifications. Moreover, the metallurgist, having learned from his microscopic studies and laboratory experiments what actually happens to steel within a furnace, knows how to regulate the process, as the steelmaker of the last century was unable to do.

Improvements in the construction and operation of the furnaces, combined with the great forward strides in the metallurgy of steel, have brought about a virtual revolution in the manufacture of the metal in the space of fifty years.

FROM CHARCOAL TO COKE

Primitive man discovered many centuries ago that by blowing air with a pair of bellows through a mixture of iron ore and wood charcoal at a high temperature in a crude furnace he could obtain a spongy lump of iron. Later, the air was blown by mechanical means, and that is the origin of the name blast furnace. Charcoal limited the size of furnaces and consumed such large tracts of woodland that the cost of transporting charcoal a long distance became prohibitive, to say nothing of the diminishing supply of timber. These handicaps forecast the end of charcoal as a major fuel for the blast furnace.

The modern blast furnace really dates from 1859 when coke began to be used as a fuel. With the use of coke it was possible to build larger furnaces. The production of coke from bituminous coal in beehive coke ovens was a thriving business until World War I gave a strong impetus to the by-product coke ovens.

BY-PRODUCT COKE OVENS

The beehive coke ovens were so wasteful that more than 30 per cent of the coal disappeared in smoke. When coal is heated in a closed receptacle, gases and vapors are driven off, leaving behind coke, a gray substance that is about 90 per cent carbon.

By-product coke ovens were first developed in Europe prior to this century, and even before 1900 several companies which later became part of U. S. Steel were utilizing by-product ovens. Since then, U. S. Steel subsidiaries have paced the industry in the size, capacity and technological developments of by-product coke ovens, which have steadily replaced the beehive ovens until today 95 per cent of the metallurgical coke produced in the United States is made in by-product ovens. In 1950, 95,000,000 tons of coal were coked in by-product ovens, producing coal chemicals valued at approximately $200,000,000. Those coal chemicals would all have been burned and lost in the atmosphere if the coal had been converted into coke in beehive ovens.

FABULOUS COAL CHEMICALS

To the scientist, coal chemicals, collectively, have been like the fabled Aladdin's lamp. It has been estimated that 200,000 useful products owe their origin to these chemicals which formerly were burned up and lost in beehive ovens.

Sulpha drugs, which have done so much to reduce pneumonia fatalities, are derived from coal chemicals. So are aspirin, novocaine, barbiturates, and certain vitamins and antiseptics. The manufacture of synthetic rubber requires the coal chemical benzol, which is also the base of the insecticide DDT. A number of soft drinks and foods owe their color and flavor to chemicals in bituminous coal. Coal chemicals are the basis for certain plastics which seem to have endless uses—telephones, radio cabinets, phonograph records, clock cases, costume jewelry, fountain pens and glass frames. Nylon, based on benzol, has many more uses than in stockings. Ammonium sulphate, another coal chemical, is

Coke for the blast furnace falls in a fiery cascade as it is pushed from a by-product coke oven into a car.

widely used in fertilizers. Toluol is the basis of the explosive TNT. Some of the other products dependent on one or more coal chemicals are: dyes, waterproofing compounds, ink, quick-drying enamels for automobile bodies and refrigerators, perfumes, adhesives, photographic chemicals, paving materials and cellophane.

EVOLUTION OF THE BLAST FURNACE

The blast furnace is one of the largest and most efficient pieces of equipment in the world for conducting a chemical operation. In the final quarter of the last century, companies that later became members of U. S. Steel's family took an active and lead-

THE COAL TREE
Some of the 200,000 Useful Products Derived from Coal

BASIC COAL CHEMICALS

BENZOL

AMMONIUM SULPHATE

TOLUOL

TAR

TAR ACIDS

Sulpha Drugs
Antihistamines
Nicotinic Acid (Vitamin A)
Aspirin
Novocaine
Barbiturates
Antiseptics
DDT
Farm Insecticides
Fertilizers
Synthetic Rubber
Waterproofing Nylon Compounds
Styrene
Food Flavors
Food Coloring
Cellophane

Viscose Casing
Laminates For Industrial Uses
Creosote Oil
Road And Roof Pitch
Can Coatings
Plastics
TNT
Adhesives
Ink
Quick-Drying Enamels
Baked Finishes On Appliances
Perfumes
Photographic Chemicals

120

ing part in improving the blast furnace. Since its formation in 1901, U. S. Steel has held a pre-eminent position in bringing about further improvements which have made the blast furnace the large and efficient producer of iron that it is today.

In the 1870's, the production of 500 tons of iron a week in a blast furnace was considered remarkable, and when 1,000 tons were recorded in one week in 1881, it was heralded as a titanic achievement. During the present century, U. S. Steel's furnaces grew larger. When the Corporation was organized it had 73 blast furnaces, with a total annual capacity of 8,333,000 tons of iron, or about 313 tons of iron daily per furnace. At present there are 81 furnaces with a total annual capacity of 26,181,000 tons of iron, or an average daily capacity of 885 tons per furnace. From these figures it may be seen that the number of furnaces has been increased by 11 per cent since 1901, while the total capacity has been multiplied more than threefold. The increase was made possible not only by larger furnaces, but also by greatly enhanced efficiency in operation. The production of 1,300 tons of iron a day by a blast furnace is now commonplace, and records exceeding 1,500 tons a day are not unusual.

TECHNICAL PROBLEMS OVERCOME

One of the technical problems encountered in the operation of the blast furnace in the early years of this century concerned the altered texture of the iron ores. When the Lake Superior iron ore mines were developed in the last century, the ores shipped to the steel mills were relatively hard and coarse. U. S. Steel's blast furnaces were built to accommodate such ores, which constituted the bulk of the iron ore charge in the furnaces. Around the turn of the century, the great Mesabi Range in the Lake Superior region was opened. Its ores were softer and

much finer than the previous ores. The finer ores did not descend uniformly within the furnace, causing a jamming and clogging of the charge. When the ores did move within the furnace, it was with explosive violence.

After more than twenty years of persistent effort, U. S. Steel completely mastered this problem. The details of this accomplishment were shared freely with the iron and steel industry. Since then, U. S. Steel has turned its attention to the development of larger blast furnaces. By 1929, one of its blast furnaces was producing 1,100 tons of iron a day, and by 1945 another furnace boosted its output to more than 1,600 tons of iron in 24 hours. Tests still going on promise still greater production rates in the blast furnace. Experts look forward with reasonable assurance to furnaces capable of producing 50,000 tons of iron a month in the not too distant future.

The introduction of mechanical methods of coal mining and the depletion of high grade coking coals presented the blast furnace operator with a problem in the utilization of coke derived from the lower grades of coal. Extensive studies and tests conducted by U. S. Steel at its coal washers and blast furnaces have mastered this problem also, thus assuring efficient peak production of the Corporation's iron and steel producing operations.

Investigations are constantly under way in U. S. Steel to improve the blast furnaces. Those receiving special attention now deal with the application of beneficiated low grade ores, the use of higher pressures in the furnaces, the value of oxygen-enriched air, new methods of introducing limestone and a host of others.

NEW ORES TO INCREASE FURNACE CAPACITY

As the steel industry presses forward to expand its steelmaking capacity, the use of beneficiated low grade ores, particularly taconite, and the rich ores to come from U. S. Steel's new mine in Venezuela, assumes added significance.

The Lake Superior ores, which have fed U. S. Steel's operations, except in Alabama and Utah, for half a century, average about 50 per cent iron content. Taconite concentrates and Venezuelan ores will run around 60 per cent iron content. Their use in blast furnaces will increase capacity without enlarging the size of the furnaces, and proportionately augment the supply of iron available for conversion into steel.

STEELMAKING FURNACES

U. S. Steel's annual capacity for the production of steel ingots and castings was 10,562,400 net tons in 1901 and 33,900,000 net tons on January 1, 1951.

Molten iron from the blast furnace flows down a trough and pours into the mouth of a ladle, seen in foreground.

A modern blast furnace, right, where initial steelmaking operations begin by smelting iron ore into molten iron.

The relative importance of the different furnaces has changed radically during this fifty-year period. In 1901, the open hearth furnaces accounted for approximately 30 per cent of the Corporation's capacity and Bessemer converters the remaining 70 per cent. No electric furnaces had been installed in the United States at that time. Fifty years later, the Corporation's open hearth capacity had climbed to 91.4 per cent, its Bessemer converters had dropped to 7.3 per cent, and its electric furnace capacity amounted to 1.3 per cent.

BESSEMERS AND OPEN HEARTHS

It is the Bessemer converter that gives the intense and fitful glow from steel mills, lighting up the night sky for miles around. This is the process, as we had occasion to observe on page 14, which introduced the modern Age of Steel. The new steelmaking method that was to revolutionize the iron and steel business was given its initial practical experiments in 1855 at a mill in Wyandotte, Michigan, owned by Captain Eber Ward. Nine years later, in the same plant, the first ingot of Bessemer steel was produced in America. Captain Ward prospered and built up the North Chicago Rolling Mill Company, which came into Illinois Steel Company, one of the founding members of U. S. Steel.

The Bessemer converter did not remain alone in the field for many years. A rival appeared in 1870—the open hearth furnace. Introduced from Europe, the first open hearth furnace in this country was installed by the Cooper-Hewitt Company of Trenton, New Jersey, one of the predecessor companies of U. S. Steel. The Bessemers, however, maintained their lead and in 1880 were the source of approximately 86 per cent of the total steel production in the United States. Most of the Bessemer converters were in eastern Pennsylvania and nearly all of their production went into the manufacture of rails. It

was, in fact, the insatiable demands of the railroads pushing westward that gave the greatest spur to Bessemer production.

In 1900, Bessemer converters in America poured from their mouths 7,500,000 tons of steel, followed in second place by the open hearths, with 3,800,000 tons. The primacy of the Bessemers was not to last much longer. In 1908, open hearth production exceeded it for the first time and the open hearth furnace has since become the work horse of the steel industry, accounting for roughly nine of every ten tons of steel poured from American furnaces.

DEVELOPMENTS IN THE BESSEMER PROCESS

One of the great advantages of the Bessemer converter is that it can produce steel in less than twenty minutes, whereas it takes eight to twelve hours to produce a batch of open hearth steel. However, Bessemer steels, because of their high phosphorus content and a somewhat higher nitrogen content, cannot compete with soft basic open hearth steels in a number of applications. On the other hand, in some fields of use, Bessemer steels give excellent service. They are superior for machining operations, lend themselves readily to welding and possess considerable resistance to corrosion.

After declining steadily for a great many years, production of Bessemer converters picked up somewhat in 1910 when it was found advantageous in certain instances to transfer the freshly-made molten steel from a converter for further refining in the open hearth furnace. Because the steel could be partially refined very rapidly in the Bessemer converter, this materially reduced the time required to complete the process in the open hearth furnace. Speeding

A Bessemer converter in full blow. This is the intense flame from steel mills which illumines the night sky.

up of the open hearth furnace operation permitted more steel to be made within a given time, which actually amounted to expanding open hearth capacity.

U. S. STEEL'S BESSEMERS

In 1901, sixteen U. S. Steel plants operated 35 Bessemer converters, with a total annual ingot capacity of 7,431,000 net tons. The vessels ranged from 5 to 17 net tons capacity, but the majority were from 9 to 11 tons capacity. U. S. Steel now has six Bessemer plants operating 17 converters. These plants have a total rated ingot capacity of 2,472,000 net tons a year, plus an additional capacity of about 4,000,000 tons annually of blown liquid steel for further conversion in open hearth furnaces. Five plants operate vessels of 28 tons capacity and one plant employs 12-ton capacity vessels.

"KILLED" BESSEMER STEEL

Perhaps the most outstanding development in the

Bessemer process in recent years was accomplished by U. S. Steel's National Tube Company at its plants in Lorain, Ohio, and McKeesport, Pennsylvania. The steel is deoxidized and is known in the industry as "killed Bessemer steel." In this new method, molten blast furnace iron is poured into the converter immediately after its fiery blow subsides. Carbon in the iron combines with oxygen in the molten steel to form carbon monoxide gas which burns off. Subsequently, additional deoxidizers are added to the steel as it is poured into the ladle. National Tube Company found that the deoxidized, or "killed" Bessemer steel was excellent for the manufacture of various kinds of pipe. Pipe made from this steel is tough, welds easily and has great strength to resist the pressure exerted on pipe, which is of particular value in the oil industry.

The method has met with such singular success that, while Bessemers were losing ground elsewhere, National Tube Company in 1949 opened a new Bessemer steel department, with three new vessels, each of 28 net tons capacity. The Bessemer converter has thereby been given a new lease on life and it is anticipated that killed Bessemer steels will find many other applications, in addition to pipe.

TURBO-HEARTH PROCESS

Of present interest are the possibilities of the turbo-hearth process applied to Bessemers. In this process, the air is blown in the side of the vessel instead of through the bottom. Steel made in the side-blown Bessemers has a nitrogen content approximately as low as that of open hearth steels. Nitrogen has a marked and sometimes undesirable effect on various steels. Since the relatively high nitrogen content of traditional Bessemer steels was one of the reasons for their restricted use, the reduced proportion of nitrogen in the steel produced by the turbo-hearth process holds promise of enlarging still further the

usefulness of Bessemer steels. Furthermore, turbo-hearth steels are made in a basic lined vessel, which reduces phosphorus content to as low as that of open hearth steels.

THE VERSATILE OPEN HEARTH FURNACE

The principal reasons for the dominant position which the open hearth furnace has gained as a producer of steel in this century are found in its great versatility and economy of operation. As the demand increased over the years for steels in thousands of different grades for the exacting requirements of modern industry, the open hearth furnace was progressively adapted to manufacture these steels in large amounts, to precise analyses, and of remarkable uniformity in quality. In a word, steel companies turned from the Bessemer to the open hearth because of the latter's greater flexibility, larger capacity and the generally higher and more uniform quality of its products. The open hearth furnace, for instance, is not generally thought of as a producer of alloy steels, but it customarily manufactures most of these steels. During World War II, when alloy steels were urgently needed in large quantities, open hearths proved their worth as producers of these steels, which amounted to almost 7 per cent of U. S. Steel's open hearth production for the years 1940 to 1945, inclusive.

The size of open hearth furnaces has been increased considerably in this century. The expansion of open hearth production in America from 3,800,000 tons in 1900 to 86,218,000 tons in 1950 has been due not so much to larger capacities as to a greater number of furnaces installed. U. S. Steel in 1901 operated 112 furnaces in 12 different plants.

Huge ladle of molten iron pours into the charging door of an open hearth furnace for conversion into steel.

One of many quality controls—an optical pyrometer records temperature of steel pouring into ingot molds.

Another quality control—samples of steel are frequently taken from the electric furnace for analysis.

Furnace capacities varied from 15 to 65 tons of steel in a single batch. The average capacity was 48 tons of steel per batch. By 1951, U. S. Steel's open hearth furnaces had increased to 313 in 18 different plants and the average capacity per batch was 140 tons of steel. It is interesting to note that three of these 18 steel plants have open hearth departments each capable of producing more steel a year than the 3,124,000 tons capacity of all the Corporation's open hearths at the time of its formation. These three U. S. Steel plants are at Gary, Indiana; South Chicago; and Homestead, near Pittsburgh.

The increased size of furnaces was accompanied by marked improvements in design, construction and control of operation. While U. S. Steel initiated many of these improvements, invaluable assistance was given to it by other industries, particularly the electrical and ceramic industries and the manufacturers of auxiliary equipment.

THE ELECTRIC FURNACE

The producer of specialty alloy steels is the electric furnace. Although open hearth furnaces manufacture the greatest tonnages of alloy steels, the electric furnace is without a peer for highly specialized steels, chiefly because it can be more rigidly regulated than the Bessemers and the open hearths. Stainless steels, heat-resistant and tool steels are made in the electric furnace, which operates with heat generated by an electric arc. The first large-scale electric furnace facilities in America were installed by U. S. Steel at South Works, Chicago, in 1909-10.

At a time when industrial America was calling for alloy steels in greater varieties and quantities for automobile parts, high-speed tools and other special applications, the electric furnace found quick favor with steelmakers. In 1913, there were 19 electric furnaces operating in the United States. The increase in the number is an index to the great growth

in American industries requiring alloy steels. By 1940, the number of electric furnaces had reached 430. They were to undergo a spectacular increase during World War II, when the number was raised to 784. U. S. Steel had a share in that wartime achievement. The American Bridge Company, one of the principal builders of electric furnaces in the United States, fabricated many of them in the war emergency. The additional furnaces, together with the open hearths, enabled U. S. Steel to boost its wartime production of alloy steels 320 per cent above 1939. U. S. Steel's electric furnace capacity on

The electric furnace produces specialty alloy steels, such as stainless steels, heat-resistant and tool steels.

January 1, 1951, was rated at 430,000 tons annually.

AUXILIARY FURNACE EQUIPMENT

Integrated steel operations are so interdependent that important changes at one stage may have to wait upon radical innovations at another. This was the case with respect to the enlargement of furnace capacities. Steel is heavy and one of the difficulties which steelmakers faced in their attempt to increase steel production was the handling of larger masses of the metal. Well into the present century, much of the steel was moved about manually.

The relatively slow growth in the size of furnaces in the first two decades of the twentieth century, especially the open hearth furnace, was due not to a lack of desire to make larger units, but to the limited mechanical facilities and auxiliary equipment available. The mechanization of such equipment through electric cranes and other means has been one of the significant advances throughout steel mills. It was accompanied by a 100 per cent increase in the average capacity of open hearth furnaces—from 50 to 100 tons per batch—between 1900 and 1920. Today, many open hearth furnaces are capable of making 250 tons of steel per batch,

and some as much as 550 tons.

To handle such large masses of fiery, molten steel pouring from the furnace, requires gigantic ladles, lifted by powerful overhead electric cranes. The ladle containing freshly-made steel is moved over ingot molds, which have also grown much larger in size. Poured into the molds, the steel solidifies into an ingot, the first solid form into which most steel is shaped.

INGOTS AND THE PRIMARY ROLLING MILLS

The ingot may be looked upon as the raw stock from which all steel products, except castings, are derived.

Massive white-hot ingot is lifted by an electric crane from a soaking pit for transfer to a primary rolling mill.

It is the traditional unit by which steel production is measured. For most purposes, the ingot is rolled into three basic semi-finished forms—blooms, slabs and billets. From these three forms, in turn, all the others are shaped in finishing mills of various kinds or by forging.

Rolling mills were rather crude and clumsy half a century ago. Now, powerful electric motors, replacing steam power, drive a huge rolling mill as a unit, in which each phase of operation is synchronized perfectly with the others. The operator, in a glass-enclosed booth, a safe distance from the hot steel, operates the rolls by manipulating control levers. The rolls can reduce the thickness of steel with a precision that was unthinkable fifty years ago. Rolling mills have been streamlined throughout, and the steel which issues from them is greatly superior in quality to the product of 1901.

FIFTY YEARS OF MAKING IRON AND STEEL

U. S. Steel's part in the colorful history of iron and steel goes back to the origins of the modern industry in America. Frequently U. S. Steel has led the way, and always it has remained in the front ranks of progress. From its furnaces during the past 50 years have come 732,000,000 tons of iron and 940,000,000 tons of steel. All over the land, this steel in every known variety and of highest quality has helped to make life healthier, more comfortable, more enjoyable, and more secure, and twice it has helped to defend our most precious heritage—democracy and the freedoms it bestows.

One of the important advances in the past 50 years is mechanization of handling equipment in the steel mills.

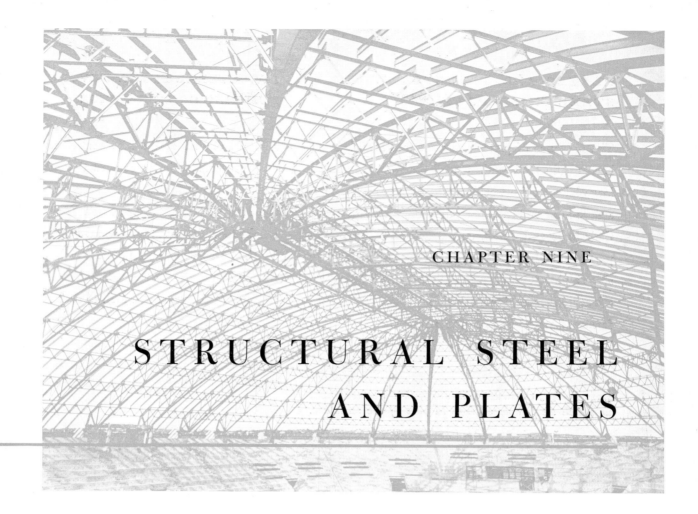

CHAPTER NINE

STRUCTURAL STEEL
AND PLATES

Probably no steel products have changed the outward appearance of America as much as structural steel and plates.

Tall buildings which form the outlines of our many cities are supported by skeletons of structural steel. The thousands of factory buildings which house the industrial might of America are constructed largely of steel framework. All over the United States, apartment and office buildings, hotels, hospitals and stores are stronger and safer because of the steel members within their floors and walls.

Modern rail and highway transportation would be impossible without structural steel and plates in the thousands of bridges which cross our rivers and streams, bays and ravines.

Tall transmission towers for electric power lines, radio and television, familiar sights in many parts of the nation, are erected with structural steel. Structural steel is entering increasingly into the construction of private homes.

There is no way of knowing how much steel in the form of plates and structural shapes exists in the buildings, bridges, dams and other structures of the United States, but the quantity is immense. It has been estimated that the buildings in the Borough of Manhattan, New York City, alone, contain 23,000,000 tons of steel, with another 1,225,000 tons in the bridges, tunnels and elevated structures.

The strength and permanence of structural steel and plates, left, are essential to construction in many forms.

A novel use of structural steel, seen above, forms a weblike pattern in the framework of a dome for a coliseum.

PLATES AND STRUCTURAL STEEL IN SHIPS

The influence of plates and structural steel has not been confined to land. On all the seas, rivers and large lakes of the world, modern vessels other than small motor and sail boats, depend on steel plates in their hulls and decks, and structural steel in supporting members. The superstructure of ocean-going ships is almost wholly steel. The swift, palatial transatlantic liner is inconceivable without these two forms of steel. Part of the armor for the Navy's battle fleet consists of heavy steel plates.

Eads Bridge, constructed in 1874, first one ever built in which steel replaced iron in part of the structure.

STRUCTURAL STEEL REVOLUTIONIZES BUILDING CONSTRUCTION

In the last half of the nineteenth century radical changes occurred in the construction of buildings in America. Until that time, masonry walls supported the entire load of the structure. This limited the height to which buildings could be safely erected. Furthermore, people did not like to climb more than five or six floors. But thickly populated cities and rising land prices caused men to search for ways to erect taller buildings.

By using a skeleton of wrought iron to support the weight of the floors and walls, it became possible to construct buildings of greater height. America's first true skyscraper was the ten-story Home Insur-

ance Building, erected in Chicago in 1888. The framework of the first six floors was made of wrought iron. Bessemer steel was coming into more general use at that time and the Carnegie Steel Company was granted permission to substitute the new steel for wrought iron in the upper four floors. Shortly afterwards, steel became the accepted structural material for tall buildings.

Taller buildings, however, were impractical without a means for people to reach floors higher than they were willing to climb. This was solved by invention of the elevator which gave a strong impetus to the construction of tall buildings. America was ready to build its towering skyscrapers.

The Carnegie Steel Company was responsible not only for the first use of structural steel in a building, but also in a bridge. The Eads Bridge across the Mississippi River at St. Louis was erected in 1874 by the Keystone Bridge Company, an affiliate of Carnegie's. A portion of the bridge was built of structural steel, marking the first time in history that steel had replaced iron for such a purpose.

In other ways, the Carnegie Company pioneered in the development and production of structural steel and made significant contributions to the use of the product. A whole new industry was in the making. So little was known about design, use and manufacture of these structural shapes that steel companies found it necessary to prepare handbooks containing engineering data for the designers of buildings and bridges. One of these, "The Carnegie Pocket Companion," first published in 1880, was the recognized textbook of structural design until recent years, when it was superseded by an industry handbook compiled by the American Institute of Steel Construction.

Since the completion of the first skyscraper in Chicago, structural steel has undergone a constant evolution in size and shape to keep up with hundreds of new applications which have arisen in this century. To fill all the demands made upon it, structural steel has been greatly improved in quality and strength and is produced in several hundred different sizes and shapes. The most familiar are the girders shaped like an "I" or an "H." Others are in the form of an "L" or a "Z," and there are many other shapes for special uses.

QUALITY IMPROVED

It is needless to stress the importance of uniform quality and dependable strength in structural steel and plates for the safety of buildings and bridges. Significant contributions in this respect have been made by U. S. Steel, which has continued the pioneering begun in the last century by the Carnegie Steel Company in the development and manufacture

of structural steel. Many of the famous buildings, bridges and other structures in America, from the San Francisco-Oakland Bay Bridge in California, the longest in the world, to the Empire State Building in New York, the world's tallest, were erected with structural steel and plates manufactured and fabricated by U. S. Steel. A list of the principal structures is given in Chapter Fourteen.

A long carpet of steel plate is gauged for thickness as it leaves the finishing rolls of a U. S. Steel plate mill.

Continuing on the conveyor, the plate is cut into sizes ordered by the customer and given further processing.

PLATES

The use of plates in combination with structural steel represents only one of the many important applications of this steel product. Wherever an exceptionally strong, economical and enduring material in a flat form is needed, a steel plate best answers the purpose. In contemporary civilization, with our many forms of heavy machinery and construction requiring great strength, such needs are never-ending.

Often these needs relate to national security. A case in point is the wind tunnel constructed by the National Advisory Committee on Aeronautics at the Propulsion Laboratory in Cleveland to test planes

traveling twice as fast as sound. The tunnel permits the testing of planes under simulated flying conditions at over 35,000 feet altitude.

Some idea of the air flow through the tunnel may be gained from the fact that, when operating at maximum capacity, two million cubic feet of air weighing almost 75 tons, are drawn through it every minute. The force of air passing through the tunnel is so great that the entrance section, or nozzle, must be flexible. The only material that could withstand the severe conditions prevailing in the nozzle and at the same time provide flexibility was stainless steel plate, one inch thick. Plates of this specification were especially made for the purpose by U. S. Steel.

PLATES HAVE MANY USES

In less dramatic fashion, steel plates help to keep modern life functioning by serving in the steam boilers of apartment and office buildings, factories, ships and locomotives; in locomotive fireboxes; in storage tanks for gases and fluids; in transmission pipelines for petroleum and gas; in railroad cars, scraper blades, power shovels and heavy machinery. The safes in which business houses and banks store their valuables are made of steel plate.

A specialty product of U. S. Steel is floor plate, which has a raised tread to prevent slipping. Such plates reduce accidents in industrial plants, on subway stairs, truck runways and loading platforms.

The rolling of plates in the opening years of this century was slow and cumbersome compared to the methods employed today. In a minute and a half, swift and powerful mills now roll a white-hot slab into a carpet of steel plate, the largest being 150 inches wide and 80 feet long. The plate is then sheared into sections. Plates vary from 3/16 of an inch to two inches in thickness. U. S. Steel has made a very substantial contribution to the practices now used in the high-speed production of quality steel plates.

U. S. STEEL'S STRUCTURAL STEEL AND PLATE MILLS

U. S. Steel manufactures plates and structural steel in mills located to serve the regional needs of the nation for such products. The newly-formed subsidiary, United States Steel Company, operates structural steel and plate mills in the Pittsburgh and Chicago districts. These mills serve principally the East and Middle-West. Southern markets are supplied by Tennessee Coal, Iron and Railroad Company, a U. S. Steel subsidiary near Birmingham, Alabama. The needs of the West for structural steel and plates are served by two subsidiaries, Geneva Steel Company in Utah and Columbia Steel Company in California.

A white-hot steel beam moves along the runway from the final shaping rolls of a U. S. Steel structural mill.

Steel girders of various shapes to help erect enduring bridges, buildings and other structures for America.

CHAPTER TEN

SHEET AND STRIP STEEL

If structural steel and plates have transformed the outward appearance of this country, it may be said that sheet and strip steel have affected the personal, day-to-day life of Americans in the past twenty-five years more than any existing material.

When a nation owns close to 80 per cent of the world's passenger automobiles and drives them 343 billion miles in one year, as the United States did in 1949, the living habits of the people to a very great extent revolve around the use of the motor vehicle. The automotive industry is the largest consumer of sheet and strip steel in the world.

The everyday life of a large portion of the population has also been transformed in a nation where 86 per cent of all wired homes have electric refriger-

ators, 87 per cent own electric irons and 72 per cent enjoy the use of washing machines, and where automatic dishwashers are in 800,000 homes and garbage disposal units in 755,000. Such was the situation in the United States on January 1, 1951. These and other home appliances are the second largest consumers of sheet and strip steel.

There are thousands of other uses. A flat, thin piece of steel can be manufactured into innumerable products—license plates, razor blades, cotton ties, door hinges, hospital sterilizers, toys, furniture, and into parts of typewriters, adding machines and a wide range of other mechanisms, both hand-operated and automatic. Coated with a thin film of tin, the sheet becomes tin plate for the preservation of food. Immersed in molten zinc, the sheet acquires a protective coating that makes it ideal for roofing material, gasoline drums and pails.

Steel products which have exerted so strong an influence on the way of life of a people caused, first

Sheet and strip steel, used in making home appliances, automobile bodies and many other products, have altered our daily living habits in America during the past 25 years more than any other material.

of all, a revolutionary change in the industry that manufactures them. The radical innovations which occurred in sheet manufacture were commented on briefly in Chapter Two. Their further explanation at this point entails some repetition.

At the beginning of the century, sheet mills were slow and laborious and their output was small. Sheets were lifted by hand and inserted into the rolls. Naturally, the amount that could be produced in this manner was limited. To make very thin sheets for tin plating, a number of sheets were placed on top of each other to form a pack, which was heated and passed through the rolls. This was necessary because the dry rolls of that process were too resilient to roll a single sheet exceedingly thin. Afterwards, workmen struggled with tongs to separate the sheets, stuck together from the pressure of the rolls.

ALONG COMES THE AUTOMOBILE

Meanwhile, the automobile industry was growing up. Wooden car bodies were not only easily shattered and highly inflammable, but they did not lend themselves readily to assembly line methods. Wood is apt to shrink and warp. Steel keeps its measurements and is vastly stronger, a safety factor of utmost importance.

The first all-steel automobile bodies appeared in 1912. Almost at once the steel industry faced a two-

As the "horseless carriages" were rapidly improved, the need arose for mass quantities of steel sheets.

The answer came in revolutionary sheet manufacture which permits shaping of body parts in power presses.

The modern automobile, safer and more serviceable, proud achievement of automotive and steel industries.

fold challenge. Production of cars in mass quantities depended upon the availability of enough sheet and strip steel at an economical price. The small output of hand-operated sheet mills made this product relatively expensive. Furthermore, the sheet steel of that period was not of a quality that would produce a suitable finish, nor could it stand the strain of being shaped into hoods and fenders in high-speed presses.

THE STEEL INDUSTRY
HAD AN ANSWER

The first problem awaiting solution was a thorough mechanization of sheet mills. This was accomplished by the development in 1925 of the continuous hot strip mill, one of the engineering marvels of modern industry. Stretching as long as a football field, the mill contains ten massive rolling stands, weighing

Continuous hot strip mill which made possible the needed production of steel sheets in mass quantities.

over one million pounds each. A ribbon of steel is passed in a continuous process through the rolls, racing at nearly 2,000 feet a minute from the end of the line, where it is wound into a large coil of strip. The continuous hot strip mill took care of the demand for volume manufacture of low-cost sheets. To clarify the discussion here, it may be pointed out that for practical purposes "sheet" and "strip" are virtually synonymous terms. Their methods of manufacture are quite similar. Their differences are largely in dimensions.

The remaining task of the engineers and metallurgists was to perfect means of further processing hot-rolled sheet and strip in mass quantities. Steel from a hot strip mill is good enough for some pur-

Cold reduction mill improves the quality of hot-rolled sheets so they can be shaped later in stamping presses.

Satiny finish of cold reduced sheets is seen in this temper mill where they are given a final processing.

poses, but in a cold condition it cannot be drawn out into complicated forms under the tremendous pressure of a stamping press without the danger of cracking. The internal structure of the steel must be modified so that the steel can "give" safely.

CONTINUOUS COLD REDUCTION MILL

One of the most spectacular advances made in sheet and strip products in the last two decades has been the development of the continuous cold reduction mill which serves two important purposes. It is so named because its powerful rolls reduce the thickness of sheet steel 50 per cent or more in a cold condition, under a pressure as great as three million pounds. At the same time, the pressure improves the steel internally so that after subsequent heat treatments it can be pressed into the rounded form of a pop-up toaster frame or the curving shape of a bathtub. Twenty-five years ago, steel could not be rolled finer than several thousandths of an inch in thickness. Now it can be rolled on a cold reduction mill as thin as one-thousandth of an inch. Cold rolling also gives a satiny, smooth finish to the steel, so pleasing in toasters, coffee makers, and automobile trim.

144

ECONOMIC AND SOCIAL SIGNIFICANCE

The economic and social significance of the modern continuous hot strip mill and the cold reduction mill can hardly be over-emphasized. Introduced at a time when the United States was moving from a capital goods economy to a consumer economy, the two new processes gave added impetus to the mass production, not only of automobiles, numerous home appliances and "tin" cans, but of products of every description in which one or more parts of sheet steel are given their form in stamping presses.

The predominant place of steel sheets in consumer articles is apparent in the fact that in the years following World War II, when manufacturing industries were trying to catch up with consumer needs, sheets were in relatively greater demand and shorter supply than any steel product.

SHEET QUALITY IMPROVED

The quality of sheets has been greatly improved and they are manufactured in many varieties of steel, including various grades of stainless steel. Metallurgists are constantly striving to improve sheets even more, and each improvement results in wider usage and greater benefit to the consumer. The application of stainless steel sheets in television tubes is one case in point. Another is the development of a grade of stainless steel which is capable of withstanding the terrific heat generated in certain parts of jet planes.

MONEY SAVER FOR ELECTRIC POWER USERS

America consumes nearly half of all the energy used throughout the world each year and the greater part of the energy consumed in this country is generated by electricity. To keep the machines of industry and business running and to furnish energy for the home and other purposes, electric utilities have grown into the third largest industry in America.

Every year additional thousands of Americans living outside of cities enjoy the use of electricity in their homes, and by the end of 1951 it is expected that 97 per cent of all the homes in America will be wired for electricity. Electricity is a cheap source of energy. In one month, the average American home can operate a radio for 24 cents, a refrigerator for 72 cents and a television set for 90 cents.

U. S. Steel has had a hand in lessening the cost of electrical power to millions of American consumers. Sheet and strip of silicon alloy steel are important materials for the manufacture of electrical generators and transformers. Silicon alloy steel was initially developed in England about 1900, and U. S. Steel was the first to introduce it commercially in the United States. When first applied here, it was estimated that silicon alloy sheets would save the users of electrical power in the United States approximately $300,000,000 a year. Since then, persistent research and experimentation by U. S. Steel have improved the performance of its electrical sheets at least 70 per cent. This important research work is conducted in several regular laboratories of the Corporation and also in a special laboratory devoted exclusively to the study of electrical sheets.

The great expansion in the use of electrical power and the improved quality of silicon alloy sheets have multiplied by several times the original annual savings to the consuming public. This could make the economies approach one billion dollars a year.

RESEARCH VICTORY IN THE NICK OF TIME

What we all know as a "tin" can is really a sheet of steel about one-hundredth of an inch thick, protected by a layer of tin one-fortieth the thickness of a human hair. More than half of all the tin cans made in the world are produced in the United States, where we turn out around 30 billion a year.

Not all the tin plate goes into the manufacture of cans, and only a little more than half of the cans manufactured yearly are used for the preservation of foodstuffs such as fruit, vegetables, meat, milk, etc. Roughly 45 per cent of can production is used as containers for paint, petroleum products, varnish, tobacco, beer, coffee, spices and a great variety of other items. Crown bottle caps, alone, account for 150,000 tons of tin plate a year, manufactured into more than 43 billion caps. Additional uses of tin plate other than cans, include baker's hardware, bread boxes, food canisters and dairy equipment, such as pails and dippers.

The traditional method for making tin plate has been to dip a sheet of steel in molten tin. This is known as the hot-dip method. Since the United States is dependent on foreign sources of tin, the known reserves of which are limited, the Corporation many years ago began to concern itself with the problem of tin conservation. It launched itself upon the formidable task of developing a process whereby tin could be deposited on steel sheets electrolytically, with a more economical use of tin. After the successful operation of an experimental pilot plant, U. S. Steel in 1937 installed the first commercial electrolytic tinning line in America, at Gary, Indiana. The anticipated savings in tin were fully borne out. The new process was found to use 60 per cent less tin than the hot-dip method. An electrolytic tinning line is a complicated apparatus about 200 feet long and costs millions of dollars.

A GODSEND TO THE COUNTRY

The electrolytic tin plating process proved to be a godsend to this country in World War II. The rapid conquest of the Malay States and the Dutch East Indies by the Japanese cut off 92 per cent of our tin supply. The situation became serious. Our armed forces and those of our allies required very large quantities of canned foods. The limited stock pile of tin in America was not enough for both military and civilian needs, and the Army and Navy naturally had first claim on the existing reserves. So critical was the situation in 1942 that the Government planned to send all canned goods exclusively to our armed forces and to allied armies through Lend-Lease. The home front would have had little or no foods preserved in tin cans but for U. S. Steel's foresight and labors of research, which were responsible for the successful commercial application of the new process.

In the emergency, U. S. Steel suggested to the Government that more electrolytic tinning lines be built as rapidly as possible and offered to share its

Electrolytic tin plating line. Process conserves tin by using 60 per cent less than older hot dip method.

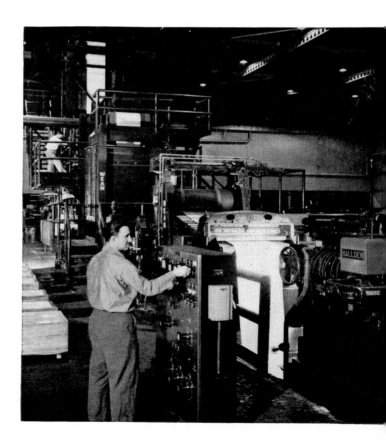

146

knowledge about the new process with other tin plate manufacturers. U. S. Steel built nine new electrolytic lines and other companies also installed them, making a total of 27 electrolytic tin plating units in this country during the war.

It has been estimated that U. S. Steel's electrolytic process saved sufficient tin in four years, from 1942 to 1945, to produce more than four and a half billion cans for packing food. That enabled the Government to spare tin for civilians, and that is why the home front, although strictly rationed, was able to buy any foods preserved in tin cans.

The electrolytic process continues to offer advantages in peacetime. It is less expensive than the hot-dip method, deposits a more even coating of tin and gives a superior product for certain purposes. Already, more than 50 per cent of the tin plate produced in the United States is coated electrolytically.

Every sheet of tin plate is inspected on both sides by women who are particularly adept at this work.

A BETTER RAZOR BLADE FOR MR. AMERICA

Up to World War II, Sweden supplied the larger part of the steel used in the manufacture of safety razor blades in America. This is no small market, when it is considered that three billion razor blades were sold in America in 1949—twice as many as in 1929. In justice to domestic steel companies, it should be added that the largest manufacturers of razor blades in America had dealt satisfactorily with Swedish steel companies for a good many years and were reluctant to break off the relationship until an American razor blade steel of proven superiority could be presented to them.

When our entrance into World War II seemed imminent, it was realized that shipments of Swedish steel for razor blades would come to an end—at least

"Tin cans" from a can manufacturer are ready to conserve food and other products for American consumers.

during the war emergency. Here was an opportunity for American steel producers. The American Steel & Wire Company, U. S. Steel subsidiary, seized it immediately. The company's metallurgists went to work and their efforts were soon crowned with brilliant success. A method was evolved which made it possible to produce razor blade steel of superior quality. As a result, this U. S. Steel subsidiary has become the world's largest supplier of razor blade steel, shipping as high as 300 tons in a single month.

Among U. S. Steel's hundreds of products, few are manufactured with as much painstaking care and receive as much attention from start to finish as steel for razor blades. It is the best steel for the purpose that science and human skill can produce.

GALVANIZED STEEL

The spangled appearance of certain pails, drums and refuse cans is due to a thin coating of zinc on sheet steel, which is called galvanizing. Next to tin, zinc is the most widely used metal to protect steel from corrosion, but it is never used for food containers.

Steel sheets are galvanized by dipping them in molten zinc. Through a recent innovation, sheet steel is also galvanized by a continuous process in which a long ribbon of strip steel is passed through a tank of molten zinc. Both processes permit the manufacture and sale of galvanized sheets at relatively low cost. That explains why they are so widely used as an inexpensive material to resist corrosive action, where stainless steel and other special steels, because of their far more complicated manufacturing processes, would be uneconomical. The weather-resistant prop-

erties of galvanized sheet steel account for its prevalence as roofing, siding, drain spouts and culverts all over America. The farmer uses this product to advantage in his sheds, coops and other buildings. In recent years, a goodly share of the grain harvested in America has been stored in bins of corrugated, galvanized steel.

The perennial rural mail box, exposed to all kinds of weather, and in which more than 30,000,000 persons in America receive their mail, offers mute but eloquent testimony to the enduring qualities of galvanized steel.

Thousands of razor blades will be made from the narrow strip steel, at left, processed with painstaking care.

Continuous galvanizing of steel sheets, right, is a recent innovation for better quality, faster production.

149

CHAPTER ELEVEN

STEEL FOR RAILROADS

Since the diminutive locomotive "Tom Thumb" made its historic run of thirteen miles from Baltimore to Ellicott's Mills in 1830, railroads have exerted a more profound influence than any other industry on the economic, social and political life of America. The railroads literally "opened up" this nation. Wherever the rails were laid down communities sprang into life and commerce thrived. When the industrial East and the agricultural Middle West were able to exchange their products by rail, America sprang forward in a burst of economic development that took it in a short period from a frontier nation to the workshop of the world.

Since the first "Iron Horses" puffed over the rails in the 1830's, drawing wooden cars, to the luxurious stream-lined train of today, progress in the railroad industry and the iron and steel industry has been closely related.

The railroads and the iron and steel industry have been intimately related since the first "Iron Horses" puffed over the rails at fifteen miles an hour, drawing rickety wooden coaches in which the passengers sat in the open, exposed to the smoke and cinders of the locomotive and with the possibility that one of the flat iron straps, serving as a rail, might come loose and protrude through the floor of the car. From that era to the shining, air-conditioned, streamlined trains of today, the story of progress in

the railroad industry is closely bound with the story of progress in iron and steel.

The railroads, eagerly pushing their steel fingers westward and southward, were mainly responsible for the enormous expansion in steel production in the last half of the nineteenth century. Andrew Carnegie was an ironmaster before he became a steel-master. It was said that he could not be persuaded to go into the production of steel until, on a trip abroad, he saw a Bessemer converter in blow. He instantly recognized the possibilities of steel rails for the rapidly expanding railroads, and it is reported that he rushed back to America on the first boat, exclaiming, "Steel is King!" He built the Edgar Thomson Works near Pittsburgh, primarily to manufacture rails of Bessemer steel. The plant, which came with the Carnegie properties into U. S. Steel on its formation in 1901, still produces rails.

A SPECIALTY OF U. S. STEEL

Steel for railroads has always been a specialty of U. S. Steel's industrial family. In addition to plates, structural steel, pipes, cable and other standard steel products, used in the manufacture of locomotives and cars, U. S. Steel makes three chief products for the railroads—rails, axles and wheels. The last-named three products are manufactured at three key points. Mills near Pittsburgh and at Gary, Indiana, are operated by United States Steel Company. These two centers supply rails, axles and wheels to the carriers in all parts of the nation, except the South, where large modern mills of the Tennessee Coal, Iron and Railroad Company take care of customers in that region.

EARLY RAIL

The first rails were thin straps of wrought iron laid on wood. Later, the entire rail was made of wrought iron. Rails illustrate in a striking manner the need for steel in mass quantities during the great railroad boom in the 1870's and 1880's. The wrought iron rail, under exceedingly light traffic, had to be replaced every two years. The modern steel rail, under very heavy traffic on a main line, has an average life of approximately eighteen years. After that it may be used for an indefinite period in secondary track.

The date of May 24, 1865, is an historic one for both the railroad and the steel industries, for it was then that the first Bessemer steel rail was rolled in America. Bessemer steel was used almost exclusively for rails until 1902, when open hearth steel was found to be a superior material for the purpose. About 1910, open hearth steel became the accepted material for rails.

The refinement in the manufacturing processes of the open hearth steel rail has been of primary importance in the expansion of the railroad industry and in the increased safety of railroad travel. To withstand the impact of heavier and faster traffic, the rail has increased in weight from 100 pounds per yard in 1900 to as high as 155 pounds at present.

MODERN RAIL MANUFACTURE

To assure that only rails of highest quality, perfect throughout, are shipped to the railroads, the manufacture of rails by U. S. Steel is conducted with the most scrupulous care. While the steel is still being made in the open hearth furnace, and at every subsequent stage of the process, samples of the steel are carefully analyzed in the metallurgical laboratory. During every step in the actual manufacture of the rails, they are closely inspected for defects. The finished rails likewise undergo a number of severe physical tests.

Railroad safety has been enhanced by a treatment given the rails after they leave the last stand of rolls, while they are still hot. Research has dem-

A shower of sparks fly in a U. S. Steel rail mill as saws cut a long rail into suitable lengths for the railroads.

Refinements in rail manufacture and careful inspection have contributed to greater safety of railroad travel.

onstrated that if rails are very slowly cooled in a controlled atmosphere, the inner stresses and strains caused by the rolling process are gradually diminished until they vanish. Such stresses and strains, if not removed, might cause tiny fissures which could enlarge into dangerous cracks.

RAILROAD AXLES

Axles are no less important than rails for safety in railroad travel. The weight of the locomotive and the cars is borne by the axles. For that reason, U. S. Steel's railroad specialists for many years have made

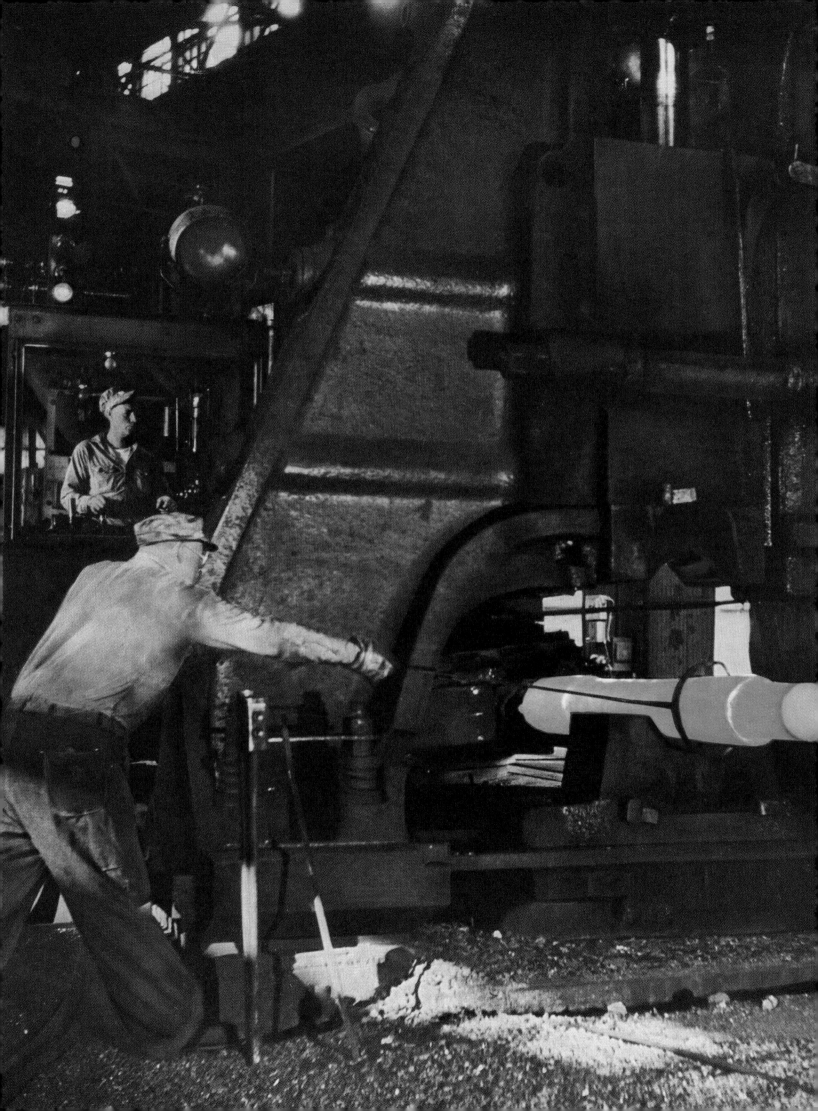

exhaustive studies of the axle—resulting in a better steel and improved manufacturing processes.

Before 1900, most railroad axles were made of wrought iron, although a small quantity of steel axles had already been manufactured. The wrought iron axles were designed for wooden cars of 20 to 30 tons capacity. With the advent of steel cars, which grew heavier, carried greatly increased loads and travelled faster, wrought iron was no longer satisfactory for axles and steel supplanted it. In 1896, the axle industry was still in its infancy and axle manufacture was not scientifically controlled. Steel that was acceptable for axles in the 1890's would be instantly rejected today.

Two years before U. S. Steel was formed, one of its predecessor companies built a new axle works, with heavier forging hammers and more efficient equipment. From then on there has been a steady improvement in the quality of axles. Hundreds of thousands of axles rendering sturdy service in locomotives, passenger and freight cars all over America were made according to the exacting specifications of U. S. Steel's axle departments.

RAILROAD WHEELS

Here is another steel product for railroads requiring the quintessence of quality for safe travel. In the early days of railroading, cast iron wheels gave fairly satisfactory service in the light wooden cars of that period. When Andrew Carnegie's company introduced a steel car of 40-ton capacity in 1896, the need for wheels of stronger material became evident. Manufacturers naturally resorted to steel. However, a small percentage of freight car wheels is still made of cast iron. Since 1915 steel exclusively has been used in manufacturing wheels of passenger cars.

Forging a railroad axle in a U. S. Steel mill. Safety requires uniform high quality in the steel for axles.

Axles for the passenger and freight trains of America being loaded for shipment from a U. S. Steel mill.

One of the stages in the forging of a railroad wheel, another specialty product of U. S. Steel for the carriers.

Railroad wheels have also been vastly improved in quality to withstand the impact of heavier and faster trains.

flaw may enlarge and ultimately cause failure if the wheel is subjected to extreme stress. What is considered a flaw in steel for railroad wheels might not be viewed as a defect for some other purposes. The precautions taken in the manufacture of wheels consist chiefly of heat treating processes, and are for the purpose of assuring absolute uniformity in quality.

The ability of modern railroad wheels and axles to withstand the relentless beating they receive from the heavy loads and thundering speeds of today has been directly responsible for the design and manufacture of railroad cars to carry loads as heavy as 70 to 90 tons. Without the refinements in rails, wheels and axles, the high-speed streamlined train would be no more than a dream on an engineer's drawing board.

There is solid reason for the steel industry's pride in its contributions to the railroads of America, which have become the safest form of transportation known to man. In ten years—from 1941 through 1950—there was one fatal accident for every 740,000,000 passenger-miles travelled. On the law of averages, this means a 100-mile journey every day for 20,300 years before the occurrence of a fatal accident in a railroad train.

As with rails and axles, U. S. Steel has striven constantly to improve the processes for manufacturing wheels. Heavier and speedier trains, and greater braking power for quicker stops, put a tremendous strain on both wheels and axles. As fast as U. S. Steel makes an improvement that meets the needs of the railroads, another pressing problem in railroad steel presents itself.

To keep ahead of the service requirements of the railroads, U. S. Steel has developed steels of special composition for wheels and devised elaborate precautionary measures for their manufacture. To have enduring and dependable strength, such steel must be of uniform quality throughout. A tiny internal

USS COR-TEN AGAIN

USS Cor-Ten was cited earlier as one example of U. S. Steel's research triumphs. This low alloy, high strength steel cannot be omitted from any discussion of steel for railroads.

Railroad trains are exposed to the corrosive effects of all kinds of weather. Copper added to steel gives it corrosion-resistant properties twice as great as those of plain carbon steel. Prolonged tests have demonstrated conclusively that USS Cor-Ten is as superior to copper steel as the latter is to plain steel. In other words, Cor-Ten has from four to six times the atmospheric corrosion resistance of plain steel and two to three times that of copper steel. For the railroads, this property of Cor-Ten means greater safety, longer life and lower maintenance costs.

Cor-Ten being stronger, weight for weight, than plain carbon steel, has made it feasible to reduce the weight of freight cars as much as 10,000 pounds. The saving in weight has two principal advantages—10,000 more pounds of contents can be carried, and the lighter cars are ideal for fast freight service which operates virtually on passenger schedules.

Over 60 per cent of America's light-weight railroad passenger equipment is built with USS Cor-Ten. By judicious use of this steel, manufacturers of passenger cars have been able to trim as much as 40,000 pounds from the dead weight of a car, without sacrificing strength or safety. This permits the more extensive use of luxury accessories.

STAINLESS STEEL IN STREAMLINERS

The bodies and much of the interior fittings of some streamlined trains are made of stainless steel. Earlier it was pointed out that U. S. Steel was the first to produce a grade of stainless steel for such purposes. In the hands of car designers the stainless steel streamliner has become a thing of sleek and shining beauty, prized by travelers who can avail themselves of its swift and luxurious service.

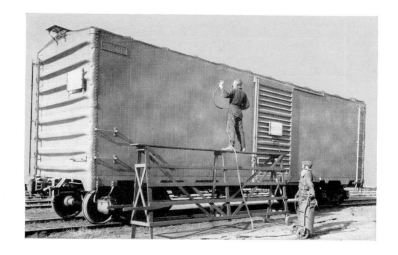

Painting a new freight car made of USS Cor-Ten, a weight-saving steel developed by U. S. Steel research.

Stainless steel interiors as well as exteriors have added to the beauty and luxury of today's streamlined train.

CHAPTER TWELVE

WIRE AND WIRE PRODUCTS

Steel wire contributes to our health, our convenience, our pleasure and our comfort. It serves the farms, every industry in the land, and is present in many forms in the home. Steel wire has 160,000 known uses. To fill the needs of all the manufacturers who buy it, wire is made to more than 10,000 specifications. Steel wire can be made hard, tough, springy or soft.

In diameter, steel wire varies from four-thousandths of an inch to nearly one inch. Probably more than one-third of all steel wire made in America is given a metallic coating, chiefly of zinc, for protective or decorative purposes. The fine bright wire used by florists is steel wire with an outer surface of green paint or bronze metal.

We rise in the morning, keep our daily appoint-

In 160,000 known uses, steel wire contributes to better living. Shown here are bundles of stainless steel wire.

ments and retire at night, according to timepieces which are "run" by hairlike steel springs made of wire, some of them so small that they weigh 30,000 to the pound. Our sleep is made more restful and comfortable by the soft yet buoyant support of steel wire springs, which also give cushioned ease in the seats of chairs and other furniture. In automobiles and trains, wire springs soften the jolts of travel and give smoother riding.

The indispensable nail is made of wire. Beside building our homes, nails have thousands of other uses, and range from tiny nails, scarcely visible, weighing 95,000 to a pound, up to giant spikes weighing nearly two pounds.

Fences of wire enclose our lands. Ropes and cables of wire supply the main supporting strength in our many graceful suspension bridges. Wire rope is also the universal material for lifting and moving heavy objects in mining, excavating, oil well drilling, manufacturing and construction and it also raises and lowers the elevators of our tall buildings.

Bolts, nuts, screws and nails, made from wire, help to hold this man-made world together. Wire paper clips and staples, in their own way, do the same.

WIRE IN AUTOMOBILE TIRES

Strands of fine wire within the bead of automobile tires strengthen the walls and add to safety on the road. Heavy duty truck tires in the future may wear 50 per cent longer, thanks to a wire specially developed by U. S. Steel for the ply, or inner fabric, customarily made of rayon or cotton. The wire, woven into strands, is almost as fine as a human hair, has a surface finish to make it adhere to the rubber and is of exceptional strength. More than 55 miles of this wire are in the cord of one tire.

In the home, steel wire appears in many forms—as pins and needles, hairpins, strainers, egg beaters, dish racks, clothes hangers, corkscrews, and bird cages. Wire screens protect our health by keeping out germ-laden flies and mosquitoes. Wound spirally and imbedded in the rubber, wire gives resilient support to the hose of vacuum cleaners.

STAINLESS STEEL WIRE IN FOOD PROCESSING

The smooth polished surface of stainless steel resists the attack of fruit and vegetable acids and offers no tiny pits for food particles to hide in. That is why it has such superb sanitary qualities and why stainless steel wire conveyors are increasingly used in food processing plants. The laws of some states require that food processing conveyors be made of this hygienic metal.

U. S. Steel has established a long and honorable record in manufacturing wire and wire products for the needs of America. American Steel & Wire Company, one of the original members of U. S. Steel, brought with it the experience and skill acquired over many years by its antecedent companies. Many inventions made by these earlier companies in the last century are landmarks in the development of the wire industry and of the nation itself.

BARBED WIRE AND THE OPENING OF THE WEST

In the colorful and dramatic story of the opening of the West a prominent place has rightfully been given to hostile Indians, bandits, swift rivers, and the hazards of weather. But another serious obstacle was faced by the pioneers trekking westward in their covered wagons in search of new homes. In the East, the settlers had found plenty of stones and wood with which to fence their lands, but in the plains and prairies there was little of either.

Settlers of the West found no material for fencing their lands. Invention of barbed wire supplied the answer.

After Congress passed the Homestead Act in 1862 to encourage the settlement of the West, a flood of migration poured westward, filling up the plains so rapidly that the problem of an adequate fence material became acute. Between 1870 and 1880 the question of fencing occupied more space in public print of the Plains and Prairie states than any other single item, political, economic or military. For a period, the settlement of the West and with it the economic progress of America were slowed down while the search went on for a cheap, satisfactory fence.

GLIDDEN INVENTS BARBED WIRE

Joseph H. Glidden, a farmer of De Kalb, Illinois, using wire to imitate the thorns of nature, invented the most practical form of barbed wire and the one most widely used for half a century.

In 1873, Glidden made barbed wire on his farm with the aid of a coffee grinder and a grindstone.

The barbs were attached by hand. With the aid of three boys, Glidden could make 50 pounds of barbed wire a day.

After some opposition from cattlemen and farmers, who feared that the barbs would injure their livestock, barbed wire caught on and its use spread like wildfire throughout the West and Southwest and eventually to all parts of the nation. To meet the soaring demands for the new product, American ingenuity invented a machine for making barbed wire and production increased by leaps and bounds —from five tons in 1874 to 40,250 tons in 1880. In 1950, the production of barbed wire in the United States amounted to 241,000 tons, enough to string 502,000 miles of three-strand fence.

Joseph Glidden sold a half interest in his patent to Isaac L. Ellwood, a hardware dealer in De Kalb. Ellwood later formed his own concern, I. L. Ellwood and Company which rapidly assumed leadership in the manufacture of barbed wire. Meanwhile, the largest wire manufacturer in America at that time, Washburn and Moen Manufacturing Company of Worcester, Massachusetts, became interested in barbed wire and bought the remaining half interest in Glidden's patent. Isaac Ellwood and John W. Gates were the chief organizers of the American Steel & Wire Company, which included Ellwood's company, Washburn and Moen and other wire manufacturers. In this way, U. S. Steel traces its long experience in barbed wire manufacture to the origins of the industry.

WOVEN FENCE AND POULTRY NETTING

The contributions of wire fence to American agriculture do not begin and end with barbed wire. Woven wire fence, with square mesh, is one of the most widely used fencing materials in the world. U. S. Steel has made great improvements in the wire and

Weaving with steel threads. Woven fence is one of the most widely used fencing materials in the world.

Chain link fence, another variety, is especially suitable for the protection of both public and private properties.

---

in the machinery used in manufacturing woven fence. It serves many purposes elsewhere than on the farm. Woven fence and another variety, called chain link fence, produced by the Cyclone Fence Division, are made in various styles to enclose tennis courts and playgrounds and to protect private and public properties.

Poultry netting is another important form of wire fencing on the farm. A great deal of this product is strung around the chicken yards and poultry farms of America.

THE INDISPENSABLE
STEEL SPRING

In this mechanical age, a steel spring is an indispensable go-between where energy cannot be transmitted—practically or economically—in any other way. A steel spring is a source of stored energy. When a spring is compressed or stretched, energy is stored in it which is released when the spring is let go. When you turn a handle to open a door it is a hidden steel spring which moves back the handle to its starting position and releases the latch when you let go of the handle. Every time you use a dial telephone you bring three springs into action—one to return the dial to a normal position after each movement, and two which regulate the speed of the dial's return so that you get the correct number.

SPRINGS IN AUTOMOBILES

The smooth functioning of an automobile requires the unfailing service of many steel springs. One popular passenger model contains over 400 springs in 180 different designs. These springs are in the clutch, the front suspension, the seats, the engine valves, the horn, the carburetor, door handles, locks, and brake release mechanism. No other spring in an automobile undergoes as much strain as the valve spring. There are two in each cylinder. In a car travelling at 50 miles per hour, each valve spring is compressed and released about 1,250 times a minute, or 75,000 times an hour. If a valve spring fails, the engine comes to a stop.

Until World War II, Swedish steel was used almost exclusively in manufacturing automotive valve spring wire. As in the case of razor blade steel, American steel circles realized that the war would compel this country to find a substitute for the Swedish steel.

In 1940, metallurgists of the American Steel &

Wire Company successfully tackled the problem. They perfected a process which produced valve spring wire of superior quality. In gruelling tests, valve springs made of the wire outlasted Swedish steel by a decisive margin. The Wire Company's accomplishment was a major war contribution, for valve springs of rugged dependability were imperatively needed to keep our jeeps, trucks, tanks and planes in operation during the conflict.

BILLIONS OF TIRELESS MUSCLES

The words of this book were originally written on a typewriter. Every time a key was pressed down, a steel spring caused the type to strike the paper and brought the key back into position. A standard office typewriter contains 178 springs and 48 other wire attachments.

One of the mechanical wonders of this age is the electronic business machine. One such machine can perform 2,174 additions or subtractions, or 79 multiplications, or 65 divisions, in one second. Absolute accuracy is a primary requisite of calculating machines. Their accuracy is amazing when it is considered that one machine has 70,000 different parts of which 4,500 are steel springs, and that the mere touch of a key will set hundreds of parts moving faster than the eye can see. Precision action is dependent, in no small measure, on the lightning movement of the steel springs.

A spring in an electric refrigerator controls the freezing unit so that the temperature does not vary more than a few degrees from that which has been set. It is a steel spring in one end of a flashlight which keeps the battery in contact with the bulb. Another kind of spring clicks the shutter in a camera, and still another, this time a flat coiled spring, supplies the motive force which turns the film in amateur and professional moving picture cameras.

These are but a few ways in which millions, even

billions, of these trusted, tireless "muscles" of steel serve us today. U. S. Steel has long been a specialist in spring manufacture and has developed many varieties of spring steel and has invented machinery with which to make this indispensable product. In most cases, springs are made to order for a specific purpose. The spring department in one of U. S. Steel's mills has made 270,000 different kinds of springs. Each varied in some degree in specifications from the others.

Two coils of a gaint spring are visible in a strength testing machine, one of many controls to assure quality.

Multiple wire drawing has increased the output. Here worker stops machine to make necessary adjustment.

One of 17 ski lifts built by U. S. Steel in the United States and Canada, enjoyed by thousands of skiers.

SKI LIFTS AND STEEL ROPE

As soon as the snow starts to fall in various regions of America, thousands of persons eagerly wait for the news that there is enough snow on the slopes for the skiing season to start. The popularity of this winter sport has skyrocketed in recent years. When skiing conditions are good, skiers converge every week end on their favorite slopes by special trains, by plane, bus and their own cars, and if possible they go where there is a ski lift.

The growing enthusiasm for skiing provided the

incentive for the construction of these aerial tramways, and they, in turn, attracted thousands more to join the ranks of skiers. An endless moving cable made of steel wire, with seats suspended at intervals, carries the skiers to the top of the slope.

The unquestioned leader in the design and construction of ski lifts and of aerial tramways of all kinds is U. S. Steel's American Steel & Wire Company. The company is responsible for seventeen passenger lifts in the United States and Canada, in-

cluding those at Sun Valley, Idaho; Cannon Mountain and Laconia, New Hampshire; Stowe and Mad River Glen, Vermont; Aspen, Colorado; Brighton, Utah; and Lac Tremblant, Quebec.

U. S. STEEL'S LONG EXPERIENCE

The American Steel & Wire Company "inherited" a rich experience in aerial tramways from the outstanding pioneer in that field, the Trenton Iron Works, of Trenton, New Jersey. Actually, the overhead conveyor system, employing wire rope, was first built in the United States on the Pacific Coast by the brilliant inventor, Andrew Hallidie, near the middle of the last century. His interest was diverted from the overhead cable system when it gave him the inspiration for his greatest invention, the street cable car.

It was the Trenton Iron Works which was chiefly responsible for making the aerial tramway system what it is today. From 1855 onward it distinguished itself by the number and importance of its contributions—new and stronger forms of cable and revolutionary features in the design and operation of aerial tramway systems. Since the company joined U. S. Steel in 1904, its pioneering work has been carried on by the Tramway Engineering Department of the American Steel & Wire Company. The overhead cable system was originally used for industrial purposes to transport raw materials and lumber, and these still constitute its chief functions. The American Steel & Wire Company has constructed 600 aerial tramways in the United States, Canada, Central and South America.

CONTINUOUS ROD MILL

Wire rope can now be made many miles in length, but there was a period in the last century when the most difficult problem facing the wire industry was to manufacture wire in long lengths—urgently needed for making into rope for suspension bridges and for use in telegraph lines. The length of wire was determined by the length of rods, the basic stock from which wire is drawn.

The crude rod mills existing at the middle of the nineteenth century produced rods of comparatively short lengths. The problem of making longer rods was solved by the invention of the continuous rod mill. In its greatly improved form today it can produce a rod more than 4,500 feet in length, capable of being drawn into a single piece of fine wire 20 miles or more long.

ICHABOD WASHBURN

Introduction of the epoch-making continuous rod mill in the United States brings up the name of the peerless wiremaker in the last century, Ichabod Washburn. He did not invent the new mill but when he saw one in England he was quick to recognize its possibilities and ordered one built for his plant at Worcester, Massachusetts. Installed in 1869, a year after his death, it was the first continuous rod mill in America.

Ichabod Washburn, however, invented much of the machinery for his plants and instituted many radical departures in wire manufacture, which enlarged the uses of wire. It was he who developed a process in this country for making piano wire at the request of Jonas Chickering in 1850. For 80 years prior to that, piano wire had been furnished exclusively by one English firm. When hoop skirts were in vogue it was Ichabod Washburn who found a way to manufacture a thin elastic wire and sell it cheap enough so that practically all hoop skirts were supported by steel wire. Starting as a poor boy, Washburn, by his inventive mind and business enterprise, raised his firm, Washburn and Moen Manufacturing Company, to an honored and eminent position. The firm brought its tradition of skill and quality products with it when it joined other wire manufacturers in forming the American Steel & Wire Company in 1899.

STAINLESS STEEL WIRE— THE REIGNING QUEEN

The story of wire is never-ending. Current uses sometimes disappear and new ones always arise. The manufacture of wire spokes for automobile wheels

Racing at 4,200 feet a minute, rods are coiled as they come from the finishing stands of a continuous rod mill.

Coils of exceedingly strong steel wire for suspension bridge cables are produced to exacting requirements.

Spinning the steel wire into cable for a suspension bridge. In all, 12,000 miles of cable wire were used.

and of springs for hand-wound phonographs was once a thriving business of the wire industry. They vanished and a hundred more uses took their place. Now stainless steel wire is the reigning queen, with an ever-growing circle of admirers. To serve the needs of its customers, U. S. Steel opened a modern

extending their services over the country in the last century, steel wire was used principally in the lines. It was to supply telegraph wire in sufficient lengths, as previously noted, that Ichabod Washburn introduced the continuous rod mill. After his death, Washburn and Moen Manufacturing Company con-

Two stainless steel rods are electrically welded into a long coil for faster drawing into stainless steel wire.

Spools of enameled copper wire for electrical coils, used in radios, T.V. sets and for other applications.

new mill in 1949 at Waukegan, Illinois, devoted entirely to the production of stainless steel wire.

The subsidiaries producing steel wire—American Steel & Wire Company, Tennessee Coal, Iron and Railroad Company and Columbia Steel Company— strive constantly to improve and vary their products for the needs of America today and tomorrow.

COPPER WIRE AND CABLES

When the telegraph and telephone systems were

tinued to be large suppliers of steel telegraph wire and, following the invention of the telephone in 1876, also manufactured steel telephone wire.

Steel wire was fairly satisfactory for such purposes, and is still used in rural areas, but in 1882 when Thomas Edison built the first electric power generating plant in New York, copper wire was needed to transmit the heavy electric loads. Copper wire, being a better electrical conductor than steel, soon became the leading material for the transmission of electrical energy.

168

When Washburn and Moen observed the diminishing market for steel telegraph and telephone wire, and saw the growing demand for power cables, they took up the manufacture of copper wires and cables. The company did not produce the copper, as it produced its own steel, but bought the copper from other companies. Washburn and Moen was manufacturing copper wire products at Worcester when it became an integral part of the newly-formed American Steel & Wire Company in 1899. The Worcester Works remains today an important supplier of electrical wires and cables, and that is how this phase of the business came into U. S. Steel.

American Steel & Wire Company was one of the pioneers in the manufacture and laying of submarine cables in long lengths, and its innovations have since maintained its prominent place in this field. The company manufactures copper wires and cables in the hundreds of varieties for our vast electrical transmission system, from giant power cables down to wire connecting a radio or television set. Some examples are trolley wire, ship cables, parkway cables for airports, athletic fields and parks, portable cables for machine shop tools, vacuum cleaners, dental equipment and soda fountains. Others are braided wires for table and floor lamps and similar fixtures where a cord of pleasing appearance is desired.

Copper wire power cable, one of the many varieties of electrical cables and cords manufactured by U. S. Steel.

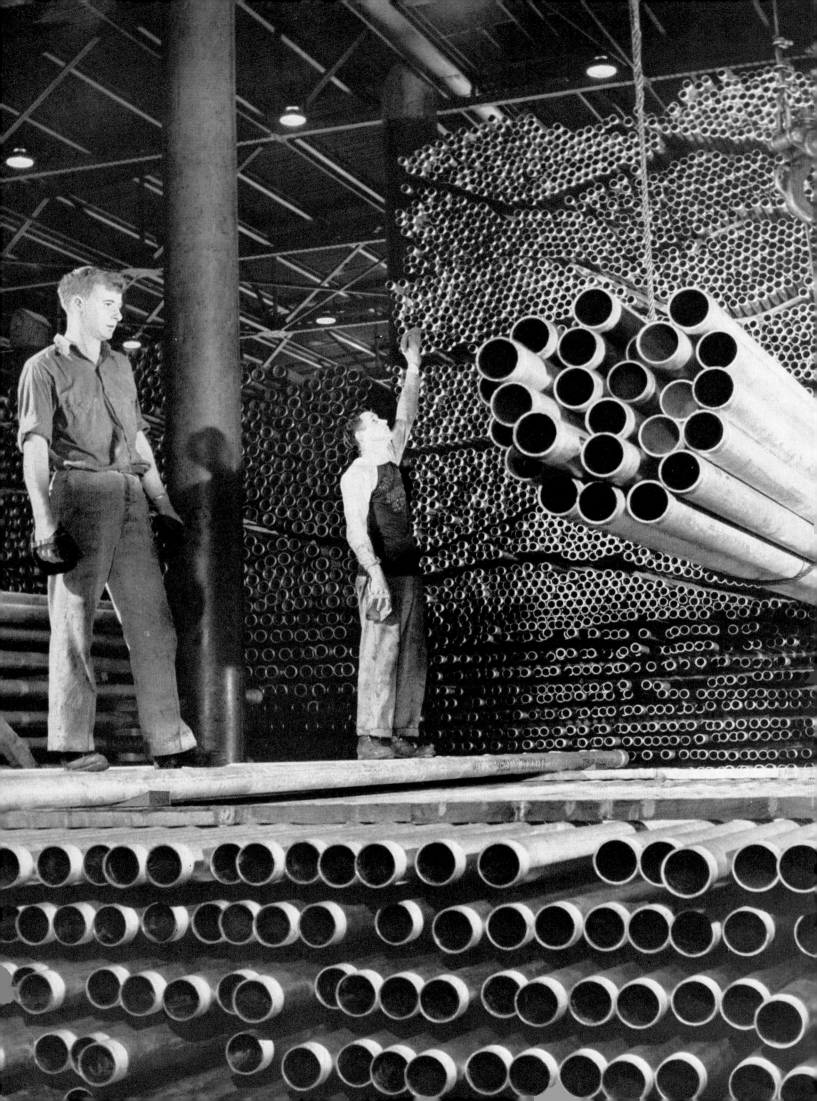

CHAPTER THIRTEEN

PIPES AND TUBES

One of the striking features of life in twentieth century America is our dependence on the daily flow of liquids and gas through steel pipes. If the water supply to a large city were cut off, the lack of water for drinking, washing, cooking and fighting fires would soon produce a major catastrophe. If the transportation of petroleum products through 152,500 miles of steel pipelines were held up for a considerable period, every automobile and Diesel locomotive would stop, every plane would be grounded and every oil-burning furnace would cease to function. Were the delivery of natural gas through 281,480 miles of steel pipelines to be suspended, many communities could not operate their cooking stoves or their refrigerators.

Refrigeration, a necessity of modern living, employs a system of steel pipes to circulate the freezing agent. We could hardly conceive of getting along without this medium to preserve perishable foods in warehouses and in our homes. Refrigeration is of priceless value to health by keeping certain serums and medicines in hospitals and drug stores ready for instant use. Fur storage vaults are maintained at their proper low temperature by refrigeration, as is the showcase of the neighborhood florist. If the flowers were grown in a greenhouse, an overhead system of steel pipes was used to water the plants.

One of the chief early uses of pipes was as boiler tubes, following the invention of the steam engine more than 150 years ago. Originally of iron, and later of steel, boiler pipes are widely found whereever steam is used for power or heating purposes. A steam railroad locomotive contains a mile of steel boiler tubing.

Modern living has become dependent on the daily flow of various fluids and gases through pipelines of steel.

The bicycle craze in The Gay Nineties led to radical improvements in the manufacture of seamless steel tubes.

PIPES IN
MANUFACTURING PROCESSES

We think of machinery as the chief agent in the manufacture of many products of everyday use, and rightly so, yet an amazing quantity of steel pipes and tubes is necessary at intermediate stages of manufacture, or in the packaging and bottling of products. This applies to drugs, soap, tooth paste

Steel pipe serves a structural purpose in the scaffolding erected for the repair of a cathedral spire in New York.

and ointments in the bathroom cabinet, many of our foods, the tires on our cars, the paper in the magazines and newspapers we read, and even to the clothes we wear.

Water in astronomical quantities, conveyed through steel pipes, is consumed in the mining and smelting of copper, zinc, lead, and other metals. A steel mill cannot operate without the accessibility

of a large source of water, and a modern, integrated plant will use 100,000,000 gallons daily.

MECHANICAL AND
STRUCTURAL PIPE

The uses of pipes and tubes, cited so far, were for the conveyance of liquids or gases. There is another and important category of uses in which these steel products serve a mechanical or structural purpose. Typical of such usages are the drive shaft, axle housing, steering column, tie rods and other parts of automobiles, which amount to 150 to 200 pounds, depending on the size of the vehicle. Elsewhere, the structural application of steel tubing is recognizable in furniture, railings, ship masts, and in trolley, flag, telegraph and telephone poles. By closing both ends, steel tubing is made into cylinders of all kinds to contain oxygen, air and various fluids.

For the purposes of discussion in these pages, pipes and tubes are virtually synonymous terms.

THE ENTERPRISING
FLAGLER BROTHERS

U. S. Steel's experience in pipe manufacture goes back to 1868, when two enterprising and progressive brothers, John and Harvey Flagler, built a small plant, 20 by 125 feet, in which to make iron products, principally boiler tubes. It was located in East Boston, Massachusetts. Convinced that their business should be located near the center of the iron and steel industry, they moved to the neighborhood of Pittsburgh and incorporated their enterprise as the National Tube Works Company.

At that time, pipe was made of wrought iron, and when the first steel pipe was produced in America in 1887, there were some who were skeptical of its future and clung to the manufacture of iron pipe. But the Flagler brothers, after prolonged investigation, foresaw a large market for steel pipe and placed the entire future of their business on their decision to manufacture steel pipe exclusively. Their decision proved to be sound and their company became the largest pipe manufacturer of that era. Integrated operation for more economical and efficient production was the order of the day, and in 1899, the Flaglers' company consolidated with other pipe manufacturers to form the National Tube Company.

This U. S. Steel subsidiary has always placed great reliance on research to improve products and enlarge markets, and it has many outstanding innovations to its credit. It has concentrated particularly on the development of seamless steel pipes and tubes.

BICYCLES, AUTOMOBILES AND OIL

Three industries exerted a strong influence on the modern pipe and tube industry. These were the bicycle, automotive and oil industries. In the 1890's a bicycle craze swept the country, creating a demand for millions of feet of seamless steel tubing for the frames which could not be met by the slow and tedious methods of tube manufacture then used. Pipe had been traditionally made by folding over a flat piece of iron or steel into the shape of a cylinder and welding the edges together into a seam running the entire length of the pipe. Such pipe was too heavy for bicycles. Experiments had been carried on since 1845 to manufacture seamless pipe, but without marked success until the 1890's. In the process finally developed, a hole was pierced through a solid round section of white-hot steel, thus forming a hollow interior without a seam.

In characteristic fashion, the National Tube Company was determined not to miss a chance to supply the market for bicycle tubes and in 1895 became the first company in America to manufacture seamless

steel tubing by the rotary piercing method. For many years the company enjoyed a large business in the manufacture of tubing for bicycles.

Then, after 1900, the automobile appeared on the scene and as its popularity increased, the market for bicycle tubes decreased. The automobile had an even more profound effect than the bicycle on the tube business. First, the steel tubing had to be of a higher quality. Secondly, the rapid increase in auto-

Seamless tube in the making — a hollow interior is made by piercing a solid round section of white-hot steel.

mobile production created a corresponding demand for gasoline, which greatly stimulated expansion of the oil industry and opened up a large new market for seamless tubes.

AMERICA STRIKES OIL

Since 1859, when the first oil well was struck in

Drake Well, where America first struck oil in 1859 at Titusville, Pa., birthplace of the petroleum industry.

America—the famous Drake Well at Titusville, Pennsylvania—the petroleum industry has grown to gigantic proportions. The monetary value of its products ranks ahead of all minerals, metallic or non-metallic. In 1949, the value of petroleum production was nearly six and one half billion dollars. Coal was in second place. Natural gas was third in value as a fuel, its production being worth a little above $1,385,000,000.

The Drake Well was only 59 feet deep and for many years oil wells did not go to any great distance in the earth. The wrought iron pipe of the period and the steel pipe which replaced it were fairly satisfactory. But in this century the oil wells went much deeper. In 1950 there were nearly one half million producing wells in the United States, the deepest reaching a little more than 15,000 feet.

The deeper wells required seamless steel pipe of greater strength than had ever been made. As an oil well is drilled by the action of a heavy steel bit, the well is lined with a casing of steel pipe to prevent collapse of the wall. The steel pipe must be exceedingly strong to withstand the pressure on its own walls at great depths, and to support the weight of a long column of casing. In rotary drilling, a steel bit may be working at the end of a column of 500 drill pipes, each 30 feet long. Furthermore, steel drill pipes are only as strong as the couplings which fasten the ends together, and the couplings are only as strong as their threads. The threads in a top joint may be required to sustain a load as heavy as a modern locomotive.

U. S. STEEL'S THREE INNOVATIONS

The National Tube Company over a period of years conducted intensive research and experimentation which resulted in the introduction of the first seamless steel drill pipe in the oil industry in 1914, followed shortly by the development of seamless steel couplings. The company also devised a new form of thread, which reduced the failure of joints, and which has since been adopted as standard for the oil industry. These three innovations have been major contributions to the drilling of oil wells.

The company subjects its seamless steel drill pipes to severe tests before shipment. Representative pipe sections are flooded with corrosive brine and rotated for weeks under bending forces up to 1,200,000-inch pounds on huge six-ton testing machines.

Unique in the world — this new U. S. Steel mill produces seamless steel pipe in one continuous operation.

174

U. S. Steel had the only plant in America capable of making 24-inch seamless steel pipe for the Big Inch pipeline.

Until the 1920's, seamless pipe could not be made larger than six inches in diameter and longer than 25 feet. As pipelines transported the major portion of oil, and petroleum production continued to climb, it was obvious that the volume flow of oil had outgrown the pipe size. Furthermore, the longer lines required greater pressure to force the delivery of oil in larger volume. The higher pressure created a need for pipe of increased strength, and this necessitated seamless pipe of enlarged diameter.

The discovery, after 1920, of huge natural gas reservoirs in remote districts, from which the gas had to be transported in steel pipelines, sometimes more than 1,000 miles, brought still greater demands on pipe manufacturers to find a way to produce pipe of larger diameter.

U. S. Steel's tube company intensified its research efforts in that direction and in 1925 developed the so-called double-piercing process, which made it possible to produce seamless pipe 16 inches in diameter. Further study enabled the company to enlarge the diameter to 26 inches and to lengthen the pipe to more than 40 feet.

BIG INCH PIPELINE

The manufacture of large diameter pipe was another research accomplishment of U. S. Steel for peacetime service to our economy which turned out to be of providential aid in World War II, when there was a serious shortage of oil and gasoline on the Atlantic seaboard, due both to the diversion of oil tankers for military service and the submarine menace. To overcome the shortage, the Big Inch line, the world's longest pipeline, was built from Texas to the New York-Philadelphia area. National Tube Company possessed the only plant in the country capable of making 24-inch seamless steel pipe.

During the war emergency, Big Inch transported

almost 362,000,000 barrels of petroleum liquids. In the words of Harold L. Ickes, then Deputy Petroleum Administrator, "It would be difficult to overestimate the part which Big Inch has played in defeating the Axis powers. It would be equally difficult to make a precise appraisal of its contributions to the victory of the United Nations and the well-being of their citizens. With other means of transporting oil inadequate, Big Inch definitely became the facility which made it possible for us to meet the petroleum requirements of the Allied armies and thus shorten the war. It likewise prevented an oil shortage on the Atlantic seaboard."

THE SPINNING METHOD

There is no way of knowing what peacetime triumph of the research laboratory will be just the one that is critically needed for national security. Another case in point was the bomb spinning method, cited in Chapter Three, and worth recalling here. Due to the initiative and skill of the Tube Company's research men, U. S. Steel in 1937 designed and built the first spinning machine in America for forming the necks of steel tubes into cylinders. A year later, the U. S. Army asked the National Tube Company to experiment with this original method in spinning the nose and tail sections of bombs, with the spectacular results described on page 56.

NATURAL GAS—
A BIG NEW INDUSTRY

The production and use of natural gas have increased at a phenomenal pace since the 1920's. In fact, a considerably greater mileage of natural gas pipelines than oil lines has been authorized or built in

Laying the Big Inch Line, which averted a serious oil shortage on the Atlantic seaboard during World War II.

On its way from Texas to southern California, a natural gas pipeline is suspended at one point to cross a river.

recent years. To handle the flow of natural gas, the need arose for pipe larger than 26 inches in diameter. To meet the need, National Tube Company and Consolidated Western Steel Corporation, a U. S. Steel subsidiary in California, manufacture steel pipe more than 30 inches in diameter. It is done by bending steel plates into a pipe form in powerful hydraulic presses and joining the edges together by automatic welding machines.

UNDERGROUND GAS STORAGE

U. S. Steel, through National Tube Company, assisted in the development of a method for storing natural gas underground, which may revolutionize gas storage. For the purpose, the company manufactured 24-inch seamless steel pipe into pressure cylinders which are buried many feet underground. One of the several advantages of the system is the elimination of hazards from airplanes, storms or rapidly changing temperatures.

Bottled gas did not enjoy its present widespread use until a process was worked out for liquefying gas on a commercial scale in 1926. Liquefied gas is marketed for home use as bottle gas, tank gas or LP-gas. As the gas in liquid form leaves the tank or bottle it is vaporized for fuel consumption. Liquefied gas is unique among fuels in that it is bought in a liquid form but consumed as a gas.

U. S. Steel's tube company has manufactured large spheres and cylindrical tanks for the storage of liquefied gas, and for the convenience of home users makes a portable 20-pound gas tank.

PROGRESS STILL THE WATCHWORD

During the past thirty years, the uses of seamless tubes have been greatly extended, calling upon the diligent metallurgist to improve and vary the steels for making tubes. Alloy steels of exceptionally high quality are required for the manufacture of races for ball and roller bearings. The race is the cylindrical section which contains the bearings.

Special alloy steels are also in demand for pipes and tubes capable of withstanding high temperatures and resisting corrosion, particularly for oil-refining, rubber, chemical and high-pressure steam industries. High-pressure steel pipes are likewise necessary in lines where the temperature is as low as 150 degrees below zero, Fahrenheit.

Alloy steel tubing for aircraft is another specialty. It is used where great strength and heat-resistant qualities are needed. Engine mounts of aircraft tubing are vital parts of a plane because they hold and support the weight of the engine. When a giant plane, weighing from 100,000 to 250,000 pounds, comes into an airfield, its safe landing depends upon steel of the utmost strength in its landing gear. The main part of the landing gear consists of seamless alloy steel tubing, which connects the body of the craft with the wheels and cushions the shock of landing. To withstand the heat generated in aircraft exhaust systems and in superchargers which supply oxygen within pressurized cabins at high altitudes,

tubing of stainless steel is almost exclusively used.

To meet all of these requirements, the steel in seamless pipes and tubes now comprehends practically the whole range of carbon and alloy steels. Research and development work in pipes and tubes never lets up, and various projects under way promise new achievements by which the industrial family of U. S. Steel will be better able to serve the nation.

Some industrial uses of pipes and tubes require steel able to withstand high temperatures and corrosive action.

CHAPTER FOURTEEN

STEEL AND CEMENT

IN CONSTRUCTION

Thousands of structures all over America are enduring monuments to the skill of U. S. Steel's structural engineers and to the scientific achievements of its specialists in cement and concrete—bridges over many rivers, tall office buildings and hotels, imposing railroad terminals, athletic stadiums, spacious airports, massive dams, shipyards, department stores, industrial plants and post offices.

The four subsidiaries rendering these services for U. S. Steel are American Bridge Company, Virginia Bridge Company, Universal Atlas Cement Company, and Consolidated Western Steel Corporation which is described in the next chapter.

Erecting United Nations Secretariat Building in New York, one of the many notable U. S. Steel structures.

AMERICAN BRIDGE COMPANY

During its fifty years as a member of U. S. Steel's industrial family, American Bridge Company has proved itself capable of fabricating and erecting any structure yet conceived by engineers. It has fabricated, or fabricated and erected, the steel for a major portion of the world's greatest bridges and tallest buildings—San Francisco-Oakland Bay Bridge, the longest ever built, the Hell Gate Bridge in New York, one of the greatest arches of all time, and the Empire State, Chrysler, Woolworth, and Rockefeller Center Buildings, all in New York.

One of the most difficult engineering tasks ever undertaken was the construction of the Panama Canal. For this vital waterway link between the

Building the Panama Canal Locks. Most of the steel and all the cement for the canal was supplied by U. S. Steel.

Rockefeller Center, New York, comprising 15 buildings, for which U. S. Steel fabricated and erected the steel.

The Orange Bowl in Miami. Athletic stadiums represent a type of structure in which U. S. Steel has specialized.

Atlantic and Pacific oceans, American Bridge Company built lock gates, dams, shop buildings and other structures.

In recognition of the company's notable accomplishments, it was entrusted with fabricating and erecting the steel for the United Nations Headquarters in New York.

ENGINEERING TRIUMPHS

American Bridge Company engineers have established a long and imposing list of contributions to the science of construction engineering. Several members of the engineering staff have gained national and international reputations in their respective fields, and a number of their books are recognized as the most authoritative writings ever published on the subjects treated. American Bridge Company is frequently consulted by outside sources on unusual and difficult engineering problems, and on many

occasions is asked to make special studies and investigations.

Following World War II, when the U. S. Army wished to preserve a certain amount of armament ready for use, it called in the American Bridge Company. Extensive research and experimentation produced an all-welded steel container, which can be hermetically sealed for the long-term storage of guns and other heavy artillery equipment. An inert gas, charged into the container and dispelling the air within, protects the equipment indefinitely. With the aid of a gas flame torch, the containers can be opened in a matter of minutes in the event of a national emergency.

During the war, the Government urgently needed a large number of LSTs—Landing Ships, Tanks—constructed in the shortest possible time. American Bridge Company applied its structural experience, with the brilliant results related on page 60.

Company engineers have greatly advanced the process of welding structural steel and the adoption of their methods has been responsible in large measure for the successful welding of steel structures, widely practiced today. Other staff engineers worked out new designs for heavy rails, which have been adopted as standard for many railroads. An American Bridge Company engineer has specialized in buildings designed to resist hurricanes and earthquakes and is well known here and abroad as an authority in his field. Still another engineer of the company has acquired an international reputation for his studies on structural steel in buildings, particularly in regard to the effects of wind. His work has resulted in a considerable improvement in building codes throughout the country.

During its many years in business, American Bridge Company has constructed practically every

Structural steel is fabricated to specifications by U. S. Steel before it is shipped to the site where it is erected.

STEELWORK BY U. S. STEEL

BRIDGES

AIRPORT & AIRCRAFT BUILDINGS

DEPARTMENT STORES

ATHLETIC STADIUMS

OFFICE BUILDINGS, HOTELS, HOSPITALS, ETC.

BRIDGES

San Francisco-Oakland Bay Bridge, Calif.
Bayonne Bridge, Bayonne, N. J.—Staten Island, N. Y.
Carquinez Strait Bridge, Crockett, Calif.
Hell Gate Bridge, East River, New York City
Bronx-Whitestone Bridge, East River, New York City
Delaware River, 2 bridges, new Delaware Memorial Bridge at Wilmington and Suspension Bridge, Philadelphia to Camden, N. J.
Henry Hudson Bridge, Harlem River Ship Canal, New York City
Marine Parkway Bridge, Rockaway Inlet, Long Island, N. Y.
Mystic River Bridge, Charlestown-Chelsea, Mass.
*Cochrane Bridge, Mobile Bay, Mobile, Ala.
Martinez-Benicia Bridge, Suisun Bay, Calif.
*James River Lift Bridge, Newport News, Va.
Commodore Schuyler F. Heim Bridge, Cerritos Channel, Los Angeles, Calif.
Mississippi River, 13 bridges, including Huey Long Bridge, New Orleans and others at Memphis, Tenn., Cairo, Ill., St. Louis Mo., and Fort Madison, Iowa
Ohio River, 23 bridges, including the Suspension Bridge at Point Pleasant, W. Va., the Louisville Municipal Bridge, the Metropolis Bridge at Metropolis, Ill., and 3 railroad bridges at Cincinnati
Pit River Bridge, Redding, Calif.
Pittsburgh, 10 bridges over Allegheny and Monongahela Rivers
Thousand Islands Suspension Bridge, St. Lawrence River, Collins Landing, N. Y.
*Yaquina Bay Bridge, Oregon Coast Highway, Newport, Ore.
*Coos Bay Bridge, Oregon Coast Highway, North Bend, Ore.
Blue Water Bridge, St. Clair River, Port Huron, Mich.
Charter Oak Bridge, Connecticut River, Hartford, Conn.
Cape Cod Canal, 2 bridges, Bourne, Mass.
Chicago River, 8 bascule bridges, Chicago, Ill.
Columbia River Bridges, 2 at Wenatchee and 1 at Vancouver, Wash.
Chesapeake City Highway Bridge, Chesapeake and Delaware Canal, Md.
Houston Urban Expressway, 5 bridges, Houston, Tex.
Kennebec River Bridge, Augusta, Me.
Lake Union Bridge, Seattle, Wash.
Michigan Central Railroad Arch Bridge, Niagara River, Niagara Falls, N. Y.
Maine State Turnpike, 40 bridges between Kittery and Portland, Me.
Mid-Hudson Bridge, Poughkeepsie, N .Y.
Newark Bay Railroad Bridge, Bayonne, N. J.

(*) *Built by Virginia Bridge Company*

Nueces Bay Causeway, Corpus Christi, Tex.
South Capitol Street Bridge, Anacostia River, Washington, D. C.
Susquehanna River Railroad, 2 bridges, Perryville, Md.
Willamette River, Portland, Ore., 2 lift bridges, and Ross Island Cantilever Bridge

AIRPORT & AIRCRAFT BUILDINGS

New York International Airport, Idlewild, Long Island, N. Y., hangars Nos. 3, 4 and 5, and 2 airplane taxiway bridges
LaGuardia Airport Marine Terminal Building, Long Island, N. Y.
Ford Motor Company Aircraft Building, Dearborn, Mich.
Goodyear Airship Hangar and Factory, Akron, Ohio
U. S. Army Airplane Hangars, Chanute Field, Rantoul, Ill.
Glenn L. Martin Company Aircraft Building, Middle River, Md.
U. S. Navy Airship Hangar, Elizabeth City, N. C.

DEPARTMENT STORES

John Wanamaker, Philadelphia, Pa.
Marshall Field, Chicago, Ill.

ATHLETIC STADIUMS

Cleveland Municipal Stadium, Cleveland, Ohio
*Sugar Bowl, New Orleans, La.
*Orange Bowl, Miami, Fla.
Yankee Stadium, New York City
Polo Grounds, New York City
*Ladd Memorial Stadium, Mobile, Ala.
Forbes Field, Pittsburgh, Pa.
Will Rogers Stadium, Broadmoor, Colo.
*Will Rogers Memorial Coliseum, Fort Worth, Tex.
*Gater Bowl, Jacksonville, Fla.
Cincinnati Gardens, Cincinnati, Ohio

OFFICE BUILDINGS, HOTELS, HOSPITALS, ETC.

New York City

United Nations Buildings
Empire State Building
Chrysler Building
Equitable Building
Metropolitan Life Building
Rockefeller Center (9 buildings)
Flatiron Building
Woolworth Building
Peter Cooper Village (21 buildings)
Crowell-Collier Building
Hudson Terminal Buildings
Irving Trust Company Building
Biltmore Hotel

Notable Structures Fabricated, or Fabricated and Erected by American Bridge Company and Virginia Bridge Company

Commodore Hotel
New Yorker Hotel
Statler Hotel

Chicago
Chicago Board of Trade Building
No. 1 North LaSalle Street
Carbide and Carbon Building
Chicago Daily News Building
LaSalle-Wacker Building
Pure Oil Building
Tribune Tower Building
333 North Michigan Avenue Building
LaSalle Hotel
Stevens Hotel

Detroit
Fisher Building
Statler Hotel
Greater Penobscot Building

Pittsburgh
William Penn Hotel
525 William Penn Place Building
Grant Building
Oliver Building

Other Cities
Cleveland Terminal Tower Building, Cleveland, Ohio
Cleveland Hotel, Cleveland, Ohio
Carew Building, Cincinnati, Ohio
Union Trust Building, Cincinnati, Ohio
Statler Hotel, Washington, D. C.
Department of Commerce Building, Washington, D. C.
Bellevue-Stratford Hotel, Philadelphia, Pa.
Atlantic City Convention Hall, Atlantic City, N. J.
Russ Building, San Francisco, Calif.
Niels Esperson Building, Houston, Tex.
U. S. Veterans Administration Hospital, Denver, Colo.
U. S. Navy Medical Center Tower, Bethesda, Md.

DAMS AND LOCKS

Grand Coulee Dam, Odair, Wash., drum gates, trestles, etc.
Hoover Dam, Boulder City, Nev., power plant buildings
Shasta Dam, Coram, Calif., material-handling tower, trestles, gates, etc.
Bonneville Dam, Bonneville, Ore., gates
*Santee-Cooper Dam, near Charleston, S. C., 60 tainter gates
Mississippi River Dams, Nos. 6, 18, 20, 25 and 26

RAILROAD TERMINALS

Grand Central Station, New York City

(*) *Built by Virginia Bridge Company*

Pennsylvania Railroad Passenger Stations:
New York City
Philadelphia (30th Street)
Pittsburgh
Union Stations: Chicago, Kansas City

U. S. NAVY YARDS

San Francisco Naval Shipyard, cranes, runways and shop buildings
Brooklyn and Norfolk Navy Yards, hammerhead cranes

POST OFFICES

Chicago, Ill.
Philadelphia, Pa.
Cincinnati, Ohio
Boston, Mass.

TOWERS

Radio Tower, Radio Station WGY, Schenectady, N. Y.
Radio and Television Research Tower and Laboratories, Nutley, N. J.
Television Tower atop Empire State Building, New York City
Thousands of miles of electric transmission tower lines throughout the United States and abroad.

OUTSIDE CONTINENTAL UNITED STATES

Panama Canal, dams, lock gates, shop buildings, etc.
Florianopolis Bridge, Santa Catharina Island, Brazil
Liard River Bridge, Alaska Highway, British Columbia, Canada
Tanana River Bridge, Alaska Highway, Tanacross, Alaska
Tanana River Bridge, Nenana, Alaska
Parana River Railroad Bridge, Brazil
Santa Lucia River Bridge, Uruguay
Isabela Bridge, Ozama River, Dominican Republic
Lempa River Bridge, Pan-American Highway, El Salvador
Hurricane Gulch Bridge, Alaska Railroad, near Anchorage, Alaska
Cauca River Bridge, Mediacanoa, Colombia
Golondrinas Arch Bridge, Columbia
Choluteca River Bridge, Inter-American Highway, Honduras
Goascoran River Bridge, Inter-American Highway, El Salvador-Honduras
Marunouchi Building, Tokyo, Japan
Atbara River Bridge, Anglo-Egyptian Sudan, Africa

known type of steel bridge, and many new engineering features introduced by the company have been landmarks in the evolution of bridge design and construction. A wire mesh catwalk, invented by the company, has added to the safety of workmen during the spinning of suspension bridge cables.

VIRGINIA BRIDGE COMPANY

Virginia Bridge Company has been a member of the U. S. Steel family since 1936. It is the largest fabricator and erector of structural steel in the South. It is noted for the versatility of its services and particularly for engineering construction of a highly complicated nature involving precision workmanship.

This latter specialty of the company qualified it eminently for the job of fabricating Bailey Bridges during World War II. Of British design, the bridge consisted of prefabricated sections which could be quickly assembled and thrown across any gap up to 240 feet, without the aid of pontoons. The Bailey Bridge has been credited with speeding the advance of Allied armies in the African and Italian campaigns and in the liberation of France. It was also used to advantage in the Pacific theatre of war.

One reason why the Bailey Bridge could be so quickly assembled was the fact that army engineers did not have to take time to fasten nuts and bolts. The joints were held together by steel pins. Since bridge erection often took place under enemy fire, rapid assembly of the sections required that they fit together with unerring precision. Since each bridge unit had to be interchangeable with units produced by various contractors in America and England, the prefabricated sections were made with the close accuracy employed in the manufacture of fine machinery. Virginia Bridge Company was ideally suited for this kind of work and was one of the principal fabricators of Bailey Bridges during the war.

ATHLETIC STADIUMS

For some years, Virginia Bridge Company has made a study of steel deck construction for stadiums and grandstands which has won it leadership in this field of structural work. Its manual on stadiums, distributed by the American Institute of Steel Construction, ranks as an authoritative guide on the subject. Outstanding examples are the Sugar Bowl in New Orleans, the Orange Bowl in Miami, and the Gator Bowl in Jacksonville, Florida.

The versatility of Virginia Bridge Company is exemplified by the type of customers it has served— railroads, mining, chemical, textile, paper and petroleum industries, state highways departments, municipalities, schools and colleges.

CONCRETE IN MODERN CIVILIZATION

Concrete, like steel, has exerted a profound influence on our way of life in the twentieth century. It has gained its eminent position as a construction material because it is economical and can be placed into any desired shape on the job site, where it hardens into a material of great durability and compressive strength. These qualities account for the fact that concrete has more than 1,000 known uses, from the relatively small basement floor of a private home to skyscrapers and massive dams. Between those two extremes, concrete is regarded as indispensable in virtually all large buildings, in highways, bridges, airport runways, dry docks, harbors and in a multitude of other major and minor projects.

Although concrete is sometimes used alone, it is generally combined with steel to form reinforced concrete. Concrete can withstand great compression, but it does not have strong resistance to pull or tension. For that reason, a grid of steel rods or a mesh of steel wires is imbedded in the concrete to resist tension, while the concrete bears the compression. In this way, concrete and steel perform the work best suited to each, constituting an effective combination for construction of many kinds.

PORTLAND CEMENT
THE BASIS OF CONCRETE

The essential ingredient of concrete is portland cement, a complex material pulverized so finely that 90 per cent of it will pass through a sieve with 40,000 openings per square inch—a sieve that will hold water. Cement is manufactured according to a precise and scientific process requiring more than 80 steps and involving the use of huge rotary steel kilns, in which temperatures exceed 2,700 degrees Fahrenheit.

The term, portland cement, owes its origin to Joseph Aspdin, of Leeds, England, who invented the first process for making portland cement in 1824. Because it resembled in color and texture the high quality stone obtained from the Isle of Portland near England's coast, Aspdin named his product "portland" cement. It has ever since been known by that name.

UNIVERSAL ATLAS
CEMENT COMPANY

The origin of U. S. Steel's manufacture of cement goes back to 1889 when a young chemist, Jasper Whiting, employed by the Illinois Steel Company of Chicago, conceived the possibility of making cement from a waste product—blast-furnace slag. He developed a successful process which he patented in 1895. To utilize the process, the Illinois Steel

Cement manufacture requires more than 80 steps, involving the use of giant rotary steel kilns, pictured below.

Company established a Cement Department. As first manufactured, the product was called "Steel Portland Cement." Mainly because of its slag content, it was not regarded by some as a true portland cement, even though there was no official definition of the term at that time. In 1898, however, a process was developed for the manufacture of an unquestionably true portland cement from blast-furnace slag and limestone, and a second plant was constructed for this purpose. In 1900, shortly before Illinois Steel Company was acquired in the formation of U. S. Steel Corporation, the trade name was changed to "Universal Portland Cement." In the following years up to 1906, when a new U. S. Steel subsidiary, Universal Portland Cement Company, was formed, two plants were built at Buffington, near Gary, Indiana. Subsequently, the company established its third plant at Buffington, also one near Pittsburgh at Universal, Pennsylvania, and another at Duluth, Minnesota, all of which continue to make portland cement from granulated blast-furnace slag and limestone.

In 1930, the Atlas Portland Cement Company, which had also been an important pioneering cement manufacturer, was joined to the Universal Portland Cement Company and the two names were combined to form the Universal Atlas Cement Company. This subsidiary has acquired and maintained a position of leadership in the cement industry by reason of its many innovations in the development, manufacture and use of the product, some of which are cited in this section.

CONCRETE ROADS

With the advent of the automobile it became necessary to find a durable surface for rapidly moving rubber-tired vehicles which quickly tore holes in gravel and macadam roads. Road builders were reluctant to use concrete, contending that it would not stand the wear of steel-tired wagons and trucks and the steel shoes of horses. A major share of credit for demonstrating the superiority of concrete for motor vehicle traffic belongs to Universal Atlas Cement Company. Due largely to the company's pioneering work, the mileage of concrete roads increased year after year.

Spacious concrete highways, usually reinforced with steel, now link our principal cities and many of our smaller communities, providing easier, safer and more pleasant riding for millions of motorists. Driving at night is safer on highways equipped with light-reflecting curb and traffic lane markers made with Atlas White Cement, developed by Universal Atlas Cement Company. The white concrete safety devices are scientifically corrugated with saw-tooth faces, which catch automobile headlight beams and reflect them back to the driver's eyes, providing a clearly visible guide for highway travel.

Universal Atlas Cement Company's research laboratories have developed new varieties of cement, which rank among the scientific achievements of U. S. Steel's industrial family for better living in America.

For a number of years Universal Atlas had sought to develop a cement that would overcome the scaling effect upon concrete pavement of alternately freezing and thawing weather and the action of de-icing salts. Success was achieved by the application of a new principle in the manufacture of cement, which resulted in the "entrainment" of billions of microscopic air bubbles within the concrete, thereby practically eliminating the scaling problem.

The new cement, introduced in 1939 under the trade name of Atlas Duraplastic, has proved its superiority over ordinary cement in millions of square yards of paving for highways, streets and airports. It has also been highly successful in the construction of skyscrapers, bridges and dams, as well as in making concrete masonry units and pipe.

OTHER CEMENT DEVELOPMENTS

Another product of Universal Atlas Cement Company's research specialists is Lumnite Cement. This is not a portland cement. Its principal constituents are calcium-aluminate compounds, instead of the calcium silicates which make up portland cement. Lumnite is the only cement of its kind manufactured in the United States.

Spacious highways of reinforced concrete are enjoyed by millions of motorists throughout the United States.

Cement, like steel, has been improved and varied in the past 50 years, largely through experimental research.

One unique property of Lumnite is its resistance to disintegration by heat. Concrete can be made of Lumnite which will withstand temperatures as high as those found in the open hearth furnace of a steel mill. This accounts for its widespread use in steel mills, oil refineries, non-ferrous smelters, ceramic factories and power plants, where high temperatures are encountered in manufacturing operations.

U. S. Steel's cement company was an early producer of white cement for the construction industry. Atlas White Cement has enhanced the aesthetic possibilities of cement in stucco, terrazzo, architectural concrete, cement paint and cast stone by combining snow-white beauty with the properties of portland cement. Its use for white concrete reflecting curb and traffic markers has been mentioned.

Cement is a necessity in oil wells, where it is used to hold the casing of steel pipes in place. Large quantities of cement are used for this purpose in the 30,000 oil wells drilled in this country annually. As wells go deeper in search of oil, special cement is required to resist the high temperatures and pressure encountered. Uniflo Oil-Well Cement, pioneered and developed by Universal Atlas Cement Company, supplies this demand.

SOME OTHER USES OF CONCRETE

Portland cement is consumed in enormous quantities in some types of construction. All the cement for the Panama Canal—8,000,000 barrels—was supplied by a predecessor company of Universal Atlas Cement Company. More than half a million barrels went into the construction of Grand Central Terminal and slightly less in Rockefeller Center. The Empire State Building required 151,000 barrels. Cement for these three structures in New York City was supplied by Universal Atlas Cement Company. Some of the dams in the United States are the world's most massive structures, surpassing in size the ancient pyramids of

Egypt, and have necessitated the pouring of concrete in gigantic amounts. Millions of barrels of Universal Atlas cement have gone into the construction of many dams, large and small, throughout America.

Thousands of miles of concrete pipe render vital services to cities and towns by conveying water to them and carrying away sewage. Concrete pipe, in irrigation systems, brings water to arid lands and increases the acreage of productive farms. Culverts and storm sewers of such pipe provide effective means of drainage.

Concrete is of great aid on American farms where it has at least 100 different uses—in silos, water tanks, feed and storage bins. Because concrete can be easily flushed and cleaned it is of sanitary value as floors in dairies, pig pens and poultry houses. Dams and retaining walls of concrete assist the farmer to conserve soil and water.

Builders in increasing numbers are taking advantage of manufactured concrete products, now produced in billions of units annually. Foremost among these are blocks, bricks and tiles. Also growing in popularity are asbestos-cement products, principally in the form of roofing shingles and siding.

ARCHITECTURAL CONCRETE

The world has traditionally looked upon concrete purely as a structural material, but in the past thirty-five years architects have begun to realize the potentialities of this plastic substance for purposes of design as well as of utility. Architectural concrete, reinforced with steel, can be cast into ornate or simple forms of great beauty. An example of ornate design is the lace-like pattern in the dome of the majestic Baha'i Temple on the shore of Lake Michigan at Wilmette, Illinois, which has been hailed as a second Taj Mahal.

Architecturally, concrete is used in two ways. It is either cast into slabs about two inches thick, away from the job site, or it is cast within moulds prepared on the site. In both cases, it is usually reinforced with a mesh of galvanized steel wire. Architectural concrete can be rendered in a wide range of colors and in mosaic designs by adding crushed

Concrete pipe made with Atlas Duraplastic, a product of Universal Atlas Cement Company research laboratory.

Promontory Apartments, Chicago, a notable example of modern reinforced concrete building construction.

quartz, granite, ceramics, vitreous enamels or color pigments to white cement concrete.

Architectural concrete slabs are adaptable to many forms of construction—the interior and exterior of public and commercial buildings, stores, theatres, homes and gas filling stations. The portico ceiling of the Department of Justice Building in Washington, D. C. is an outstanding example of interior application. The twenty-story Administration Building and other structures of the U. S. Naval Medical Center near the Capital, at Bethesda, Maryland, exemplify the exterior use of concrete slabs.

Architectural concrete, which is cast into form on the job, originated on the Pacific Coast and its use has spread to all parts of the country. One of the finest examples of its use is in the Pentagon Building, headquarters of the War Department in Washington and the largest office building in the world.

191

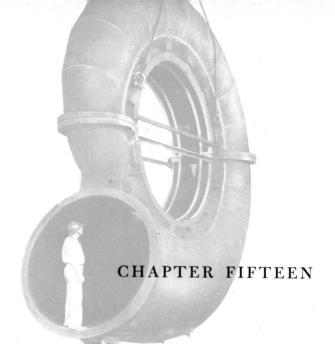

CHAPTER FIFTEEN

FABRICATING SERVICES

Every manufacturing enterprise seeks to vary its services and thereby enlarge its markets. Some steel producers, including U. S. Steel, fabricate a number of their basic steel products, such as plates, sheets, pipes and wire for specific needs of their customers. In the preceding chapter the fabricating work of U. S. Steel's two bridge companies was described. Other fabricating services of a specialized nature are performed by five members of U. S. Steel's industrial family—Consolidated Western Steel Corporation, Oil Well Supply Company, U. S. Steel Products Company, Gerrard Steel Strapping Company and Gunnison Homes.

In 1854, five years after the Forty-Niners poured frantically into California in search of gold, the Francis Smith Company set up a small shop in the mining town of Grass Valley, California, to produce water pipe for gold miners. The iron pipes carried water to wash the gravel deposits containing the precious metal. This company was the forebear of the Consolidated Western Steel Corporation. The name "Consolidated" originated in 1928 when three pioneer structural steel fabricating firms of southern California were merged into one company. "Western" was added to the name in 1945 after the company acquired a large plate and sheet fabricator known as "Western." U. S. Steel had steel-producing facilities in the West in Columbia Steel Company and Geneva Steel Company, but lacked fabricating services there of the kind rendered by Consolidated Western. To round out its services to the West, U. S. Steel acquired Consolidated Western in 1948.

Steel fabrication takes many forms — one of nine steel shells to enclose a highway under a Texas ship channel.

Above, part of a hydroelectric turbine, one of the many specialty jobs fabricated for western power projects.

YOU NAME IT—
WE'LL MAKE IT

Consolidated Western Steel Corporation is a general fabricator of plate and structural steel and of mechanical equipment for western and southwestern states and export markets. It also manufactures electric welded pipe of large diameters and welded freight car underframes. Most of the company's work is made to the order of a customer, and there is no way of telling what job the company may be called upon to fabricate next. Its slogan might well be, "You name it—we'll make it." Its orders have varied from the fabrication of circular steel shells over 34 feet in diameter and totaling nearly one-half mile in length, forming the inside of a vehicular tunnel, to the fabrication and erection of the revolving steel dome for the Palomar Observatory near San Diego, housing the world's largest telescope.

CONSOLIDATED WESTERN'S
WAR SERVICE

During World War II, the fabricating experience and facilities of Consolidated Western Steel Corporation and constituent companies were of immeasurable value in the national defense program. The company operated several Government shipyards in addition to its own plants and demonstrated its versatility by building 23 types of vessels, including flat-tops, destroyers, destroyer escorts, troop transports, cargo ships, icebreakers and landing craft. The total deliveries amounted to 1,429 vessels, of which nearly 900 were landing craft vitally needed in the Atlantic and Pacific theatres of war.

The icebreakers constructed by Consolidated Western for the Navy were novel in design and operation. They were equipped with a propeller in the bow, as well as two in the stern. The heavy bow could be driven up onto the ice. By shifting the bal-

last a rocking motion was produced in the bow which broke the ice. The action was aided by reversing the forward propeller, creating a turbulence which helped to buckle the ice. The new icebreaker did valiant war service in arctic regions and two of them, owned by the U. S. Coast Guard, plowed the way through ice twelve feet thick for Admiral Richard Byrd's expedition to the Antarctic in 1947.

IRRIGATION AND
WATER SUPPLY

Adequate water supply has long been a problem in parts of the West. Most of the richest agricultural lands have insufficient rainfall and must receive additional water through irrigation projects. As population increased, it became necessary for Los Angeles, San Francisco and other municipalities to reach across the state to the Sierra Nevada Mountains and to the Colorado River to obtain more water. Dams and long pipelines were built to furnish water for both needs. In this phase of the West's development, Consolidated Western has played a conspicuous role. It has fabricated locks, gates, valves, and construction trestles for many of the dams. Since most of the dams were harnessed to generate electricity, a need arose for high pressure steel pipe, called penstocks, as large as 18 feet in diameter, to carry the water to the turbines which drive the electric generators. Consolidated Western has fabricated these penstocks to generate power and large diameter pipe for aqueducts to transport the waters of the West. These extra-size steel pipes fabricated from steel plates are a specialty of Consolidated Western.

Consolidated Western pioneered in the development of steel pipe 26 to 31 inches in diameter especially designed and constructed for long gas and oil transmission lines. In this country they have been of great benefit to communities in New York and California by increasing the flow of gas in transmission lines from Texas to those two states.

TRANS-ARABIAN PIPELINE

Consolidated Western's new large diameter pipes have recently played a prominent and dramatic role in the Middle East, where they were used to build the 1,068-mile Trans-Arabian Pipeline from the Persian Gulf side of Saudi Arabia to a port on the Mediterranean Sea. The line, opened in December 1950, in effect moved the vast Arabian oil fields 3,500 miles nearer to European and eastern United States markets. This reduction in distance is effected by the pipeline crossing the Arabian desert to the Mediterranean, obviating the need of oil tankers to make the 3,500 mile trip around Arabia, up through the Red Sea into the Suez Canal and then into the Mediterranean. By saving tankers a voyage of 20 days and 7,000 miles round trip formerly required, the new pipeline is expected to release more than 65 ocean-going tankers for needed service elsewhere.

The capacity of the line is 300,000 barrels of crude oil a day, moving at the rate of two and a half miles an hour through pipes of 30 and 31 inches in diameter. The importance of this greater accessibility of oil in large quantities to the United States, especially in times of national emergency, need hardly be stressed.

OTHER SPECIALTIES OF CONSOLIDATED WESTERN

Consolidated Western has recently added to its facilities a production line for the fabrication of welded railroad freight car underframes. The volume manufacture of this new product is of particular value in helping to overcome the serious shortage of freight cars in the present emergency.

Other tailor-made fabricating jobs of Consoli-

Another specialty is the fabrication of large diameter pipes from steel plates to carry water to the turbines.

dated Western include a supersonic wind tunnel for testing planes at simulated speeds faster than sound, built for the California Institute of Technology; giant rotary kilns for the manufacture of cement; smoke stacks, and forms for lining tunnels with concrete.

With numerous brilliant achievements to its credit, this company looks forward to still greater accomplishments in sharing the future growth of the vigorous and dynamic West and Southwest.

"EVERYTHING FOR OIL WELLS"

In the 1890's an advertisement appeared in American newspapers which read: "Everything for Oil

A production line has been added to western operations for the fabrication of welded freight car underframes.

Wells; Any size; Any depth; Anywhere."

This was published by the Oil Well Supply Company and the claim still holds good. The company's name and the slogan imply just what this U. S. Steel subsidiary does—supplies "everything," which means machinery, pumps, drilling rigs and other equipment for which the need may arise in an oil or gas field, from a rivet to a 7,000-pound drilling bit, and from a 30-cent oil can to a 55,000-barrel storage tank.

OIL WELL SUPPLY COMPANY

Oil Well Supply Company was born three years after the first commercial oil well was drilled in America. The company has grown with the industry and has made so many important contributions for economical, efficient production of oil, especially in wells of great depth, that a history of the company occupies an important place in the history of the petroleum industry. Since 1930 Oil Well Supply Company has been a member of U. S. Steel.

In the early years of the petroleum industry, wood was used in the derricks, in various parts of the drilling and pumping equipment and even in the storage tanks. The change from wood to steel was gradual. The first complete steel derrick was built by the Carnegie Steel Company in 1907 at the suggestion of Oil Well Supply.

The expense and time involved in drilling oil wells are factors in the cost of the gasoline you buy to run your car and the oil and grease which lubricate it. The significance of this statement comes home when it is realized that the petroleum industry drills about 30,000 wells a year in America, many of which are more than 10,000 feet deep. Only two-thirds are usually productive, but the other one-third must be drilled just the same. The average cost of drilling a well is $45,000 but some have cost as much as one million dollars. The greatest drilling footage

196

in history was accomplished in 1950, when more than 30,000 miles were drilled, enough to equal seven oil wells drilled to the center of the earth.

FASTER, DEEPER DRILLING

Oil well drilling was done for a great many years by what is termed the cable tool method. In this, a heavy, chisel-shaped steel bit is lifted and let fall again and again. Through sheer force of weight, the drill forces its way into the earth. As it became necessary to drill wells deeper and wider, a new method was developed, called rotary drilling. The drill rotates like an auger and bores its way into the earth. Now almost all drilling is done by the faster and more economical rotary method. U. S. Steel's oil well company was among the first in the nation to design and manufacture the rotary machinery and necessary tools.

In the drilling of an oil well, high pressure pumps are required to circulate a mixture of mud and water through the drill pipe to remove the cuttings from the auger bit. The rate of removal, which varies with the earth formations encountered, determines very largely the speed of the drilling. Oil Well Supply Company holds a prominent place in the development, manufacture and distribution of slush pumps, another major contribution to efficient drilling.

PUMPING THE OIL

Once a well has been drilled, contrary to popular belief, oil generally does not flow to the surface, but must be pumped. Even if the oil does rise naturally, the flow eventually stops and the oil must be raised by pumps or other mechanical means. A pump cylinder is lowered within the tubular steel casing to the

Oil well derrick, the steel framework which supports the drilling equipment, familiar sight in the oil fields.

Pumping machinery developed and manufactured by U. S. Steel for greater efficiency in oil operations.

Sucker rods leaving a heat treating furnace, an important process for greater strength and uniform quality.

level of the oil. The piston of the pump is connected to a string of slender steel rods—called sucker rods —reaching all the way to the surface. The piston is moved up and down by the sucker rods which receive their motion on the ground level from a "walking beam" as it bobs up and down like a mechanical grasshopper.

Originally, sucker rods were made of wood, connected with wrought iron rings. Next, the rods were made of wrought iron. When wells reached 4,000 feet, stronger sucker rods were needed and in 1908 Oil Well Supply revolutionized the sucker rod industry by introducing the all-steel integral joint sucker rod, which is still the basic design in use today.

The quality of steel in sucker rods is an important factor in the cost and efficiency of oil well pump-

198

ing. The slender rods, reaching thousands of feet, are subjected to tremendous strain. Each sucker rod must be capable of carrying loads up to 45,000 pounds per square inch. Uniform quality of the steel is imperative, because, like a chain, the string of sucker rods is no stronger than the weakest rod.

Here, again, Oil Well Supply met the severe requirements of the industry by subjecting the rods to careful heat treating processes, which resulted in stronger rods, uniform in quality throughout. Their success in operation was outstanding.

Meanwhile, another problem plagued the oil industry. In some of the deepest wells, sucker rods of ordinary, or carbon steel, could not resist the corrosive action of certain fluids encountered. U. S. Steel's Oil Well Supply Company met the challenge by introducing a new steel which has given phenomenal performance in pumping deep wells where corrosion is severe.

OIL WELL FIELD STORES

In the infancy of the oil industry, producers maintained a stock of machinery, tools and equipment in their own warehouses near operating centers. But this was found to be uneconomical, and oil companies began to rely on supply houses. As part of its service to the oil industry, Oil Well Supply distributes its products through stores and warehouses conveniently located near large producing districts, both in the United States and in foreign countries.

DRUMS AND PAILS

The petroleum industry relies mainly on steel throughout its operations, from drilling wells to delivering its products to consumers. Tankers, pipelines, tank cars and tank trucks, made chiefly of steel, transport a large volume of petroleum and its products to their ultimate destinations. But for

many purposes, the most expedient way to ship finished petroleum products, particularly lubricating oil, greases and kerosene, is in steel drums and pails.

The steel shipping container business owes its origin to the petroleum industry. When the oil boom originated in the last century, the traditional wooden barrel was adopted as a shipping container. But the barrels often leaked or broke and oil producers explored the possibilities of steel barrels. The first appeared about 1902 and by the end of World War I they had largely replaced the wooden barrel as a shipping container for petroleum products. The steel barrel evolved into the steel drum, the former having a bulge at the middle and the latter having straight sides, which is a more convenient shape for shipping and storing purposes.

The principal purchaser of steel drums is still the petroleum industry, which absorbs about 60 per cent of the annual production ranging from 20,000,000 to 27,000,000 units in recent years. Twenty per cent

Completing a 55-gallon steel drum, one of the many kinds of steel shipping containers made by U. S. Steel.

are used for shipping chemicals, 10 per cent for foods, 5 per cent for paint and 5 per cent for miscellaneous products. The paint industry is the principal buyer of steel shipping pails, of which an average of 60,000,000 are manufactured yearly.

U. S. STEEL PRODUCTS COMPANY

From 1915 onward, some steel producers undertook the manufacture of drums as an added outlet for their steel sheets. The trend was more pronounced after the continuous hot strip mill expanded sheet production, and by 1939 most of the large steel companies of the nation had entered the steel container industry. U. S. Steel joined their ranks in that year with the acquisition of a new subsidiary, Boyle Manufacturing Company. In 1943, the company name was changed to United States Steel Products Company. Later in that year, and again in 1944, two other drum manufacturers were added to U. S. Steel Products Company.

With six plants strategically located, U. S. Steel Products Company is able to serve the regional needs of its principal customers—oil refining and chemical companies. Future plans include a plant on the East Coast to serve the markets in that area.

U. S. Steel Products Company manufactures drums and pails in sizes ranging from one to 110 gallons. The 55-gallon drum and the 5-gallon pail constitute about 75 per cent of the company's business.

A small percentage of drums and pails is used for the shipment of products whose corrosive effect on steel would contaminate or discolor the contents. To protect certain products from corrosive action, some of the containers are galvanized. In instances where the utmost protection against contamination

For a number of purposes, steel pails are galvanized to withstand corrosive action, such as these refuse pails.

is required, drums and pails are made of stainless steel to ship products, such as soft drink syrups, essential oils for perfume and many industrial acids.

For market gardens and for home use on the West Coast, U. S. Steel Products Company manufactures in California a line of garden tools, wheelbarrows, galvanized ware and painted housewares.

STRAPPING WIRE AND STRAPPING MACHINES

Baby chicks, fresh fruits and vegetables, flowers, canned goods, furniture, bicycles, automobile parts and thousands of other items are shipped daily throughout the United States. Their safe delivery requires containers of many kinds—cartons, wooden boxes and crates of sundry shapes and sizes, and huge cases for industrial materials. Experience has proved that the best all-around reinforcement to hold such containers intact is steel strapping wire.

It is not always practical, for one reason or another, to ship articles in containers. Instead, they are bound with wire strapping. Newspapers, as they come from the presses, are stacked in bundles and bound with steel wire for delivery to newsstands or for shipment to other towns and cities. Large bulky industrial materials, such as culvert pipes, heavy machinery, steel rails and lumber are fastened securely by strapping wire in freight cars to withstand the shocks of long hauls.

GERRARD STEEL STRAPPING COMPANY

In 1917, the Gerrard Wire Tying Machine Company began on a small scale to manufacture a simple wire tying machine. It was an unexplored business and the company, by its ingenious inventions, led the way in the use of steel wire strapping. It introduced a semi-automatic, portable strapping machine, elec-

A semi-automatic machine for tying round strapping wire is closely inspected by an experienced workman.

Magazine bundles are speedily and securely tied by a wire strapping machine for delivery to newsstands.

trically operated, which can make 15 to 18 ties a minute. The machine is widely used for strapping packaged containers as they come from the production line in manufacturing establishments and for the speedy bundling of newspapers. In addition to manufacturing strapping machines, the company sells strapping wire for use in the machines.

The Gerrard Company first joined the U. S. Steel family in 1937 as a subsidiary of the American Steel & Wire Company. Six years later it was established as a separate U. S. Steel subsidiary under the name of Gerrard Steel Strapping Company.

FREE FALL CARGO

During World War II, Gerrard's products were invaluable for packaging supplies for the Army and Navy—ammunition cases, boxes of canned foods, medicines and many other items. On numerous occasions, troops were isolated from their main base, or, as paratroopers, were deliberately put down behind enemy lines. The only way to supply these men was from the air.

How would it be possible to drop medicine vials and other delicate objects, undamaged? The problem was brought to the Gerrard Steel Strapping Company. A method of securely strapping a wooden box was devised. It was the wire and the shape of the box that did the trick. One of the chief difficulties was in developing a wire that was strong enough to hold the box intact as it hit the ground and bounced 30 feet in the air, and yet had enough elasticity to absorb the shock of the fall. As is so often the case, the steel had to have just the right properties. But all problems were mastered. In preliminary tests, eggs were dropped in a box from planes in flight without breaking the shells.

Called free fall cargo, the boxes safely delivered food, medicine, ammunition and other military supplies from the air. Released at an altitude of 200 to 250 feet, the boxes could be deposited with great accuracy. A wire cutter attached to the box enabled it to be opened in a few seconds. In peacetime, free fall cargo can be extremely valuable in delivering supplies to isolated communities, especially in times of flood or other disasters.

Since the war, Gerrard Company has considerably improved its strapping machines for faster packaging of materials for shipment and has widened the application of strapping wire. The new uses include the swift and economical packaging of bread in returnable cartons, bundling of magazines, and the strapping for carload stowage of items ranging from automobile glass and bricks to steel sheets.

GUNNISON PREFABRICATED HOMES

The prefabricated home, assembled on the site from factory-made parts, is the answer to the need of many people for a low-cost dwelling. In the hands of an experienced designer and manufacturer, such a home can combine the latest features for comfort and convenience with durability and beauty.

Gunnison Homes fit this description. After years of research and a thorough study of architectural design in small homes and of prefabricating methods in this country and Europe, Gunnison Homes, Inc. began manufacturing in 1936. As was the case with its entrance into other fabricating operations, U. S. Steel recognized in the prefabricated home the potentialities of a new market for various fabricated steel products. Gunnison Homes, Inc. was acquired in 1944 as a new subsidiary.

The Gunnison Home is fabricated in standardized, interchangeable parts. The panels are made on the stressed-skin plywood principle. The prefabricated sections can be rapidly put together on the site. One of the homes in the low-cost category has been enclosed, the roof panels erected and the door

The Gunnison Home is prefabricated in standardized, interchangeable parts for rapid assembly on the site. The homes are produced in two models, conventional and ranch-type, in sizes from two to three bedrooms.

locked within five hours.

Originally, the company made two homes, the Master, in the lower price bracket, and the DeLuxe, in the higher price range. Since 1949, these two types have been superseded by the Champion and the Coronado, the latter introduced in 1950. These Gunnison Homes come in five sizes. Champion No. 1 is the smallest. It has two bedrooms. Champion No. 2 also has two bedrooms, but is a slightly larger house. Champion Nos. 3, 4 and 5 are three-bedroom dwellings.

RANCH TYPE GUNNISON HOME

The Coronado is a low-cost ranch type home, featuring low pitched roofs, overhanging eaves, sweeping horizontal lines and large picture windows. It is designed to meet the large demand for a ranch type dwelling in the low-cost home field and sells in the

$7,000 to $10,000 price range. The Coronado Home, introduced in 1951, is available in five sizes containing two and three bedrooms.

All Gunnison Homes lend themselves to a variety of external architectural treatments. When completed, they contain streamlined steel kitchen cabinets with double compartment sink, modern bath facilities and large rooms with ample closets. Every Gunnison Home is completely insulated, has automatic hot water and a forced hot air furnace for gas or oil fuel.

Numerous housing projects are composed exclusively of Gunnison Homes. One of the largest is a community of 500 units in a suburb of Louisville, Kentucky.

CHAPTER SIXTEEN

WORLD WIDE SERVICE

In the closing years of the last century, before U. S. Steel was formed, one of Judge Gary's arguments for integrated steel production was that the anticipated economies would permit competition on favorable terms in foreign markets, thereby enlarging outlets for domestic steel production and stimulating America's export trade.

While it is true that U. S. Steel, its employees and the nation as a whole have gained through the business and jobs created by the Corporation's foreign sales, the advantages have not been one-sided. The steel exported has contributed materially to world progress, benefiting peoples in many lands in the same way that the basic metal has contributed to our own industrial growth, for U. S. Steel does more than export its products. Drawing on its wealth of knowledge and experience gained in serving all

U. S. Steel serves world progress with steel products, shipped in Isthmian Steamship's ocean-going vessels.

branches of our economy, it consults with foreign customers and advises them concerning their needs. When the needs have been determined and agreed upon, subsidiary companies manufacture the steel to specifications and fabricate it ready for use or assembly. Engineers and other technicians abroad supervise the construction work and often furnish their own crews with American know-how.

AN EXPORT COMPANY FORMED

After U. S. Steel was organized, the member companies continued to carry on independently the foreign business which they had already established. This was soon seen to be both uneconomical and impractical and in 1903 it was decided to channel all foreign business to one organization. Accordingly, the U. S. Steel Products Export Company was created. Its name eventually was shortened to U. S. Steel Export Company. Since its inception, the Export Company has handled approximately 69,000,000 tons of U. S. Steel's products, valued at more than four billion dollars.

A serious obstacle encountered by the company in its early years was the shipment of U. S. Steel's products overseas. It became more and more difficult to secure cargo space. The American merchant fleet was inadequate for our overseas commerce. Freight rates charged by foreign-owned vessels were very high. Furthermore, cargo space was often unavailable in both American and foreign vessels, and as a result, U. S. Steel's products often had to lie at seaboard for days and weeks, and even months, waiting for steamers willing to accept them. The long delays caused inconvenience and increased costs, especially to foreign customers, and this situation, though unavoidable, was not conducive to good business relationships.

Isthmian Steampship vessels take U. S. Steel products to many foreign ports. One of the ships at Calcutta.

ISTHMIAN STEAMSHIP COMPANY

To surmount the difficulty, the Export Company in 1908 decided to buy and operate its own ships. The company began with nine steamers and subsequently chartered others in order to take care of U. S. Steel's growing volume of foreign sales. Later, it was considered advisable to have the fleet operated by a separate company and this task was entrusted to the Isthmian Steamship Company. The name, Isthmian, was selected in honor of the Panama Canal, which crosses the isthmus separating the Atlantic and Pacific oceans.

After the first World War, U. S. Steel owned two large shipyards which had been busily engaged in building vessels for the Government during the conflict. Two alternatives were open, either to close the yards or to find a constructive use for them. U. S. Steel chose the latter course and built 28 ships for its own use, specially designed to accommodate all types of steel products and other classes of cargo not ordi-

narily carried in the average vessel, as well as general shipments. Later, the Isthmian line was obliged to charter vessels to meet the demands for its services, extending to ports all over the globe. On return voyages, the ships bring essential imports, chiefly raw materials, from the far corners of the earth.

These, then, are the two agents—U. S. Steel Export Company and Isthmian Steamship Company—through which U. S. Steel serves world progress with products of steel. The Export Company, with customers in more than 70 countries, including nations of almost every tongue and creed, functions as the agent between the foreign customer and the Corporation's steel producing and fabricating subsidiaries. Isthmian, sailing the seven seas, takes the products in many instances to the customer's nearest port. Both have collaborated in many important services, in peace and in war.

The story of economic progress in many foreign countries is reflected in the types of products which U. S. Steel has been called upon to supply through the Export Company since the turn of the century: rails, railway accessories and bridges for the construction of railroads to open up vast regions in China, South Africa and South America, so that the products of the soil and the mines could be brought to seaports for shipment to other nations; materials with which to build power plants and electrical transmission lines for growing cities and industries; tin plate for the flourishing canneries of Australia, Argentina, Portugal, Japan and the Scandinavian countries; tubular steel products for the development of large oil-bearing regions in Mexico, the Caribbean area, Indonesia and the Middle East; bridges and cables for modern highways, such as the Inter-American highway through Central and South America, the Central Highway in Cuba and a cut through the Andes in Peru, linking to the sea the great fertile plains east of the mountains.

New railway bridge over Corinth Canal, Greece, part of rehabilitation program serviced by U. S. Steel.

LOCUST PLAGUE IN ARGENTINA

Wherever steel has been required and whatever the need, the technical and engineering skills and productive facilities of U. S. Steel have been ready to promote better living in many parts of the world. Sometimes, the services have been of an emergency nature. During the 1920's, a locust plague struck Argentina. In the vast pampas, hordes of the insects would consume the grain in a whole area during a single night and then move on. Every fifteen days, the locusts laid their eggs, which matured rapidly, leaving behind new armies of destruction. The Argentine Department of Agriculture found that the most effective means of combating the invaders was to erect a barrier of galvanized steel sheets, eighteen inches high. Where could large quantities be obtained while there was still time to save the remaining crop? The answer was—from the rolling mills of U. S. Steel, thousands of miles to the north.

The Export Company was charged with the order, the largest ever placed for galvanized sheets—enough

Colombia's tallest building, at Bogota. The structural steel was fabricated and erected by U. S. Steel.

to erect 14,000 miles of barriers. Thirty-five days after receipt of the order, the first shipment reached Buenos Aires, eighteen of the days having been consumed in transit by fast steamer. The balance of the order speedily followed. Erected for miles across the path of the marauders, the sheets were too smooth for the young to climb and too high for them to jump over. In deep pits dug before the barriers, millions of the pests piled up and died. Thanks to man's ingenuity, and steel delivered in time, large areas of the crop were saved.

HELPING TO WIN THE WAR

In World War II, the Export Company and Isthmian

To augment sources for oil in World War II, U. S. Steel supplied steel for new oil projects in Venezuela.

Liard River Bridge, one of many over the Alcan Highway linking Canada to Alaska, built by U. S. Steel.

were powerful instruments in bringing materials and equipment for the construction of bases for the defense of the Panama Canal and the Western Hemisphere and advance bases in all theatres of war. To prepare some of those virgin areas for construction of defense posts was itself a herculean task for the Army and Navy, requiring heavy steel equipment for earth removal, grading, filling and dredging, building bulkheads and docks. Then the base had to be built—barracks, recreation halls, hospitals, storehouses, landing strips, hangars, control towers, power plants, telephone and lighting systems and even railroads in some cases. Afterwards, our forces, everywhere abroad, had to be constantly reinforced with supplies. A large portion of the steel products

needed for all these purposes was expeditiously handled by the Export Company and carried by Isthmian Steamship Company vessels.

In the form of Lend-Lease, millions of pounds of munitions and food and other supplies went to strengthen the fighting arm of our allies. The Export Company's war service began in June 1940, after the British had evacuated Dunkirk and the democratic world waited to see where Hitler would strike next. There were signs that he planned the invasion of England. History has since revealed that England was ill-prepared to resist invasion, having sent virtually all of its combat equipment earlier to the Continent, where it was destroyed in the Battle of France or abandoned on the beaches of Dunkirk.

GUNS FOR EMBATTLED BRITAIN

In those dark days, the Chief of U. S. Army Ordnance summoned Irving S. Olds, Chairman, and Benjamin F. Fairless, President, of U. S. Steel overnight to Washington. He proposed that U. S. Steel buy various surplus munitions—artillery, rifles, machine guns, ammunition, etc.—in Army arsenals, valued at $41,000,000 and resell them to the British and French Governments. The U. S. Army was not

first shipload of munitions sailed for Britain. By the end of the month the final load was on its way. All ships arrived safely, bringing critically needed help to the last bastion of freedom in Europe.

WATER FOR THE BATTLE OF EGYPT

In another hour of need—this time in the Middle East—the Export Company rushed through an order

Construction of hydroelectric plant in Uruguay for which U. S. Steel supplied numerous steel products.

to be paid in cash, but in new munitions of an exactly equal value, of its own selection.

U. S. Steel agreed, and the Export Company was assigned responsibility for overseeing shipment of the munitions. On June 7, 1940, the historic "Exchange Contract" was signed. Four days later the

for the construction of a water pipeline in Egypt. The campaign in Africa had been under way since the spring of 1940 and by December the Axis forces were approaching the Great Desert which stood between them and Egypt. An order came to U. S. Steel from England for 150 miles of pipeline complete with fittings, and 50 Diesel-driven pumping units, to bring water to the British forces at the fighting front.

The entire job was to be completed and loaded

aboard ship within six weeks. Before some of the work could even begin in the plants of Oil Well Supply Company, which handled the contract, time had to be taken to design the special pumping units and write instructions for their use. The complete order, totalling 38 carloads, reached the port on schedule. The Export Company and Isthmian saw to its safe delivery.

In desert fighting, water is as vital as food and ammunition. By supplying British Tommies with

the U. S. Merchant Marine. Sometimes, when a shipload of U. S. Steel's products went to the bottom, the mills had to duplicate a carefully manufactured order. Isthmian Steamship Company played an heroic role in delivering supplies to every war front. Isthmian ships participated in every important invasion, step by step, from North Africa, Sicily, Italy, and Southern France, to Normandy in the European zone and from Leyte and Guam to Attu in the Pacific theatre. During these operations, numerous crew

drinking water in the burning desert sands, the pipeline was a vital factor in Field Marshal Montgomery's defeat of Marshal Rommel in the Battle of El Alamein, which saved the Middle East and was one of the decisive turning points in the war.

ISTHMIAN IN THE WAR

Sinkings by Axis submarines put a heavy burden on

Steel for China, some years before Korean war. Coolies hauling U. S. Steel products through Shanghai.

members perished and the company lost 22 ships.

As an agency of the War Shipping Administration, Isthmian operated the largest merchant fleet sailing under the American flag. From the time the war began until December 1941, the company brought to America large tonnages of essential ma-

213

terials which disappeared from import trade after Pearl Harbor. During that period it was responsible for 60 per cent of the crude rubber and half of the tin imported into this country, as well as other strategic alloying metals.

BOMB ALLEY

After the German attack on Russia, the United States rushed to the aid of the Soviets with enormous Lend-Lease supplies. At first, the only avenue open to Russia was by sea to Murmansk. Isthmian ships and men braved the dangerous run of "bomb alley" as this northern route to Russia was called. Lend-Lease shipments to Russia were later augmented by deliveries to the Persian Gulf and overland transportation to southeastern Russia. Isthmian vessels carried all Persian Gulf shipments.

ISTHMIAN SINCE THE WAR

To rehabilitate its damaged fleet, Isthmian purchased after the war 24 C-3 type ships from the U. S. Maritime Commission. The ships are much larger and faster than those in prewar service.

The C-3 type ships are equipped with radar for greater safety at sea, always of paramount importance to Isthmian Steamship Company for the protection of passengers, crew, the vessels themselves, and the cargo, often valued at six to seven million dollars and occasionally exceeding ten million dollars in one voyage.

TRANS-ARABIAN PIPELINE

In the preceding chapter, mention was made that Consolidated Western Steel Corporation manufactured all the pipe for the 1,068-mile Trans-Arabian Pipeline. Isthmian Steamship Company transported the pipe, together with other equipment and supplies,

from California to unloading points on the Persian Gulf and the Mediterranean, involving voyages of 11,890 and 9,360 miles respectively.

The 600,000 cargo tons of pipes, equipment and other supplies had to flow steadily in order to keep pace with the work of the field crews. Isthmian discharged its responsibilities on schedule, and in so doing carried out one of the largest marine commercial transportation jobs on record.

ISTHMIAN ERIE BASIN BREAKWATER TERMINAL

The time required for a ship to make a turnabout in port, unloading and loading cargo, has a bearing on the efficient and economical conduct of business by a steamship line. Likewise, the facility with which shipping companies can obtain or leave deliveries at ship side is a factor in the charges which they must make for their services.

The large new Isthmian Erie Basin Breakwater Terminal, opened in Brooklyn, New York, in 1951, provides terminal facilities not surpassed in efficiency and economy by any steamship company in the Port of New York with operations comparable to those of Isthmian. Four C-3 type Isthmian vessels can be accommodated at one time.

The terminal is less than ten minutes motor driving time from the Brooklyn end of the New York-Brooklyn Vehicular Tunnel, inaugurated in 1950. Each of the four fireproof sheds contains platforms where trucks can deliver and pick up cargo at tailboard level, a feature that will save them considerable waiting time, a sizable cost factor to the shipping public in the New York area. At the same time, the loading platforms and other facilities of the terminal enable Isthmian to mechanize its operations to a maximum degree. Adequate arrangements are provided at the terminal for the delivery and removal of cargo by railway and barges.

Pipe fabricated by U. S. Steel for Trans-Arabian Pipeline, being unloaded from a U. S. Steel vessel.

The old world and the modern meet in the desert during construction of the 1,068-mile Trans-Arabian Line.

CHAPTER SEVENTEEN

DEPARTMENT STORES
FOR STEEL

About five-sixths of the steel sold in the United States is delivered directly from the producing mills to the customers, usually in volume lots. But there are tens of thousands of steel users whose day to day needs are relatively small and for whom it is impractical to buy in carload quantities. It is essential to our economic well-being that steel in many forms and sizes be accessible in small amounts to these thousands of manufacturing, construction and business companies throughout the nation. Warehouses constitute their chief source of supply.

To serve the requirements of its customers whose purchases are weighed in pounds instead of tons, U. S. Steel maintains fourteen warehouses, located

From 14 warehouses, such as this one, U. S. Steel serves its customers who need steel in small lots.

in the chief industrial centers from coast to coast, operated by U. S. Steel Supply Company. The majority of the Supply Company's nearly 40,000 customers are small businessmen, who buy steel for their manufacturing needs or for maintenance and repair purposes. The remaining customers are large firms who normally buy directly from the mills, but who occasionally require small lots of steel.

A warehouse of U. S. Steel Supply Company is to the purchaser of steel what the department store is to the general public. The customer of a warehouse may choose from a stock of more than 5,000 varieties and sizes of steel, plus an assortment of industrial supplies and metal-working machinery. If the steel he desires is readily available, he may be able to have his order filled within an hour or two after placing it.

The Supply Company's warehouses do far more than keep on hand a stock of plates, girders, pipes, sheets, rods, wire and so on. An integral part of their service is to shear, saw, or flame-cut material into various lengths, sizes and intricate shapes, according to the customers' specifications. The company also distributes metal-working tools, supplies and machinery to such customers as boilermakers, sheet metal and welding shops.

In the construction of reinforced concrete projects the need often arises for the quick delivery of reinforcing steel. Six warehouses of the company are

Warehouses are equipped to fabricate various shapes and sizes of steel to the customer's specifications.

equipped to supply reinforcing steel, fabricated to specifications, to contractors of projects such as buildings, dams, bridges, roads and other reinforced concrete structures.

ORIGIN OF U. S. STEEL SUPPLY COMPANY

U. S. Steel Supply Company was an outgrowth of the famous rolling mill built in North Chicago in 1857 by Captain Eber B. Ward for the purpose of re-rolling old iron rails. In this mill the first steel rails were rolled in America in 1865.

North Chicago Rolling Mill Company was one of several steel concerns that went into the formation of the Illinois Steel Company in 1889. How the Illinois Steel Company was later brought into U. S. Steel has been related in Chapter One.

After it became part of the Illinois Steel Company, the North Chicago rolling mill continued to manufacture steel rails for the burgeoning railroad industry. Later, when large integrated mills were built in the Chicago area, the production of steel was discontinued at the North Chicago plant and it was converted into a warehouse, called the Illinois Steel Warehouse Company, to handle the large volume of orders received for steel in small quantities. It was in this way that Captain Ward's mill became the nucleus of U. S. Steel's warehouse service. To extend this service to thousands of other customers on a nation-wide basis, U. S. Steel acquired and built additional warehouse facilities over the years. Since 1943, they have been under the management of U. S. Steel Supply Company.

Steel vitally needed to convert military planes for combat duty is rushed from a warehouse to a plane.

Stocked with steel in 5,000 varieties and sizes, a warehouse is a "department store" to a steel buyer.

218

TABLES

UNITED STATES STEEL CORPORATION

PRINCIPAL SUBSIDIARIES

COMPANY ADDRESS	PRESIDENT
American Bridge Co., 525 William Penn Place, Pittsburgh 30, Pa.	F. K. McDanel
American Steel and Wire Co., Rockefeller Bldg., Cleveland 13, Ohio	H. B. Jordan
Bessemer and Lake Erie Railroad Co., Union Trust Bldg., Pittsburgh 30, Pa.	Fred W. Okie
Birmingham Southern Railroad Co., Brown-Marx Bldg., Birmingham 2, Ala.	H. E. Parker
Bradley Transportation Co., 2050 Guardian Bldg., Detroit 26, Mich.	Irvin L. Clymer
Carnegie Natural Gas Co., Frick Bldg., Pittsburgh 19, Pa.	Dan S. Keenan
Columbia Steel Co., Russ Bldg., San Francisco 6, Cal.	Alden G. Roach
Consolidated Western Steel Corp., Box 2015, Terminal Annex, Los Angeles 54, Cal.	Alden G. Roach
Duluth, Missabe and Iron Range Railway Co., Wolvin Bldg., Duluth 2, Minn.	P. H. Van Hoven
Elgin, Joliet and Eastern Railway Co., 208 So. La Salle Street, Chicago 4, Ill.	T. D. Beven
Geneva Steel Co., Box 269, Salt Lake City 8, Utah	Walther Mathesius
Gerrard Steel Strapping Co., 2915 West 47th Street, Chicago 32, Ill.	H. G. Walter
Gunnison Homes, Inc., Charlestown Road, New Albany, Ind.	John J. O'Brien
Isthmian Steamship Co., 71 Broadway, New York 6, N. Y.	W. M. Wells
Michigan Limestone & Chemical Co., 2050 Guardian Bldg., Detroit 26, Mich.	Irvin L. Clymer
National Tube Co., 525 William Penn Place, Pittsburgh 30, Pa.	J. E. Goble
Oil Well Supply Co., 2001 North Lamar Street, Dallas 1, Tex.	Fred F. Murray
Oliver Iron Mining Co., Wolvin Bldg., Duluth 2, Minn.	R. T. Elstad
Orinoco Mining Co., 25 Broad Street, New York 4, N. Y.	Mack C. Lake
Pittsburgh & Conneaut Dock Co., Conneaut, Ohio	K. C. Stevens
Pittsburgh Steamship Co., Rockefeller Bldg., Cleveland 13, Ohio	W. C. Hemingway
Tennessee Coal, Iron and Railroad Co., Brown-Marx Bldg., Birmingham 2, Ala.	A. V. Wiebel
Union Railroad Co., Union Trust Bldg., Pittsburgh 30, Pa.	Fred W. Okie
Union Supply Co., 1509 Muriel Street, Pittsburgh 3, Pa.	F. R. Walton
United States Steel Co., 525 William Penn Place, Pittsburgh 30, Pa.	Benjamin F. Fairless
United States Steel Export Co., 30 Church Street, New York 8, N. Y.	George W. Wolf
United States Steel Products Co., 30 Rockefeller Plaza, New York 20, N. Y.	John Hauerwaas
United States Steel Supply Co., 208 So. La Salle Street, Chicago 4, Ill.	L. B. Worthington
Universal Atlas Cement Co., 100 Park Avenue, New York 17, N. Y.	Blaine S. Smith
Virginia Bridge Co., Box 2201, Roanoke 9, Va.	F. K. McDanel

*Typical of clean, safe, modern working conditions is
this mill for manufacturing concrete reinforcing bars.*

OFFICERS AND DIRECTORS

Board of Directors	IRVING S. OLDS *Chairman* ARTHUR M. ANDERSON SEWELL L. AVERY JAMES B. BLACK CASON J. CALLAWAY PHILIP R. CLARKE BENJAMIN F. FAIRLESS	C. JARED INGERSOLL WILLIAM A. IRVIN NATHAN L. MILLER ALEXANDER C. NAGLE GEORGE A. SLOAN HERBERT E. SMITH MYRON C. TAYLOR ENDERS M. VOORHEES
Finance Committee	ENDERS M. VOORHEES *Chairman* ARTHUR M. ANDERSON BENJAMIN F. FAIRLESS WILLIAM A. IRVIN NATHAN L. MILLER	ALEXANDER C. NAGLE IRVING S. OLDS GEORGE A. SLOAN HERBERT E. SMITH MYRON C. TAYLOR
Officers	BENJAMIN F. FAIRLESS *President* IRVING S. OLDS *Chairman of Board of Directors* ENDERS M. VOORHEES *Chairman of Finance Committee*	MAX DON HOWELL *Vice President and Treasurer* ROBERT C. TYSON *Vice President and Comptroller* WM. AVERELL BROWN *Secretary*
Counsel	NATHAN L. MILLER *General Counsel*	THOMAS F. LYNCH *Assistant General Counsel*
Offices	51 Newark St., Hoboken, N. J. *Principal Office*	71 Broadway, New York 6, N. Y. *New York Office*

Former Presidents, Chairmen of Board of Directors and of Finance Committee

Presidents	CHARLES M. SCHWAB	April 6, 1901 — August 4, 1903
	W. E. COREY	August 4, 1903 — January 31, 1911
	JAMES A. FARRELL	January 31, 1911 — April 19, 1932
	WILLIAM A. IRVIN	April 19, 1932 — January 1, 1938

Chairmen, Board of Directors	ELBERT H. GARY	April 9, 1901 — August 4, 1903 (a)
		August 4, 1903 — August 15, 1927 (b)
	J. P. MORGAN, JR.	December 27, 1927 — March 29, 1932
	MYRON C. TAYLOR	March 29, 1932 — April 5, 1938
	E. R. STETTINIUS, JR.	April 5, 1938 — June 4, 1940

Chairmen, Finance Committee	ROBERT BACON	April 9, 1901 — November 12, 1901
	GEORGE W. PERKINS	November 12, 1901 — February 26, 1907
	ELBERT H. GARY	February 26, 1907 — August 15, 1927
	MYRON C. TAYLOR	December 27, 1927 — January 1, 1934
	W. J. FILBERT	January 1, 1934 — January 1, 1936
	E. R. STETTINIUS, JR.	January 1, 1936 — April 5, 1938

(a) *Executive Committee.*
(b) *Board of Directors.*

STATISTICAL SUMMARY

FIFTY YEARS OF BUSINESS

		Cents of Sales Dollar
Receipts to January 1, 1951		
Products and services sold	$49,254,000,000	—
Disposed of as Follows		
Employment costs	20,277,600,000	41
Products and services bought	17,512,500,000	36
Wear and exhaustion of facilities	3,185,700,000	6
Interest and other costs on long-term debt	933,300,000	2
Income and other taxes	3,283,000,000	7
Dividends		
Preferred stock	1,278,200,000	2
Common stock	1,427,000,000	3
Income reinvested in business	1,356,700,000	3
	$49,254,000,000	$1.00
Production and Shipments		
Production—Ingots and Castings	net tons	939,800,000
Shipments—steel products	net tons	665,100,000

THEN AND NOW

		Then 1902†	Now 1950	Per Cent Change
Capacity	Ingots and castings			
	Net tons	11,237,000	33,869,000*	201.4
	% of industry	44.2	32.5*	— 26.5
Production	Ingots and castings			
	Net tons	10,920,000	31,457,000	188.1
	% of industry	65.2	32.5	— 50.2
Shipments	Steel products			
	Net tons	8,913,000	22,635,000	154.0
Employment	Average number of employes	168,127	288,265	71.5
	Average hourly earnings	$0.201	$1.828	809.4
	Average weekly earnings	$13.75	$69.10	402.5
	Average weekly hours	68.4	37.8	— 44.7
Stockholders	Preferred stock	25,296	74,119	193.0
	Common stock	17,723	197,778	1,015.9

*January 1, 1951.
†First Calendar Year of Operations

U. S. Steel's Operating Story 1902*-1950

Net tons in thousands

Year of oper.	Total ores mined	Total fluxes produced	Total coal mined	Total coke produced	Total iron produced	Ingots & castings Total production	Ingots & castings % Capacity operated	Steel products shipped	No. of employees	Weekly hours	Hourly earnings	Weekly earnings
1902*	17,991	1,471	13,813	9,522	8,933	10,920	97.2	8,913	168,127	68.4	$.201	$13.75
1903	17,207	1,421	12,660	8,658	8,153	10,275	81.8	8,129	167,709	66.6	.207	13.79
1904	11,763	1,560	13,718	8,652	8,254	9,422	72.8	7,325	147,343	67.4	.192	12.94
1905	20,705	2,203	17,228	12,243	11,393	13,447	93.2	10,142	180,158	68.9	.198	13.64
1906	23,123	2,495	18,533	13,295	12,619	15,153	100.6	11,254	202,457	68.6	.204	14.00
1907	26,858	3,585	24,279	13,545	12,794	14,944	88.6	11,511	210,180	68.5	.214	14.67
1908	18,662	2,448	15,799	8,170	7,767	8,779	50.3	6,820	165,211	65.1	.214	13.92
1909	26,243	3,916	23,790	13,590	13,013	14,958	77.8	10,612	195,500	68.8	.216	14.85
1910	28,275	5,606	26,365	13,650	13,251	15,881	79.5	11,777	218,435	68.4	.224	15.33
1911	22,326	5,416	24,326	12,120	12,034	14,284	70.5	10,340	196,888	67.2	.234	15.73
1912	29,600	6,859	30,639	16,719	15,889	18,929	89.8	13,771	221,025	69.0	.238	16.41
1913	32,187	7,099	30,787	16,663	15,770	18,655	90.1	13,387	228,906	68.9	.252	17.35
1914	19,079	5,238	21,162	11,174	11,259	13,246	62.3	9,935	179,353	67.6	.257	17.38
1915	26,510	6,491	26,628	14,501	15,278	18,342	85.2	12,826	191,126	68.3	.260	17.76
1916	37,358	7,866	32,768	18,902	19,721	23,420	100.6	17,105	252,668	68.8	.290	19.94
1917	35,596	7,274	31,497	17,462	17,531	22,719	91.9	16,919	268,058	69.2	.359	24.85
1918	31,733	5,758	31,748	17,758	17,854	21,934	88.2	15,570	268,710	66.1	.489	32.33
1919	28,474	6,536	28,893	15,464	15,274	19,264	77.0	13,470	252,106	59.1	.617	36.48
1920	30,264	6,699	30,828	16,208	16,277	21,591	86.2	15,534	268,004	59.4	.699	41.55
1921	18,646	5,160	21,628	9,825	9,720	12,282	48.3	8,758	191,700	61.0	.546	33.30
1922	24,392	6,309	23,293	13,237	13,470	18,012	70.9	13,127	214,931	64.5	.446	28.78
1923	34,737	7,365	35,290	18,838	18,737	22,770	89.1	15,870	260,786	59.3	.583	34.54
1924	27,747	5,638	27,738	14,408	14,206	18,456	72.2	12,705	246,753	52.8	.650	34.29
1925	31,357	5,986	31,476	16,301	16,575	21,167	81.7	14,753	249,833	53.7	.653	35.04
1926	32,778	6,175	34,295	17,336	17,590	22,743	89.1	15,771	253,199	53.7	.660	35.42
1927	28,725	5,215	27,430	14,507	15,438	20,705	79.8	14,310	231,549	53.6	.666	35.68
1928	29,834	16,352	28,691	15,993	17,066	22,518	84.6	15,400	221,702	52.2	.684	35.70
1929	34,214	16,535	31,827	17,355	18,463	24,493	90.4	16,813	254,495	46.2	.685	31.67
1930	27,211	16,365	25,388	13,113	14,289	18,762	67.2	12,798	252,902	43.2	.686	29.66
1931	15,233	8,595	15,575	7,041	7,864	11,292	37.5	8,399	215,750	34.4	.690	23.74
1932	4,050	3,587	7,047	2,966	3,498	5,521	17.7	4,324	164,348	25.4	.614	15.58
1933	9,347	6,060	10,227	4,880	5,629	9,013	29.4	6,354	172,577	30.4	.596	18.14
1934	11,283	6,769	11,724	5,382	6,174	9,700	31.7	6,501	189,881	30.2	.705	21.26
1935	12,810	7,842	15,095	7,328	8,307	12,467	40.7	8,086	194,820	33.9	.731	24.77
1936	21,306	12,031	23,581	12,034	13,501	18,937	63.4	11,905	222,372	39.6	.737	29.16
1937	34,080	14,696	24,504	14,190	16,171	20,756	71.9	14,098	261,293	37.6	.864	32.51
1938	12,303	7,818	13,842	7,006	7,632	10,525	36.4	7,316	202,108	29.7	.902	26.80
1939	24,225	12,852	21,624	12,092	13,656	17,626	61.0	11,707	223,844	35.2	.897	31.59
1940	34,047	15,730	29,528	16,144	18,367	22,934	82.5	15,014	254,393	36.7	.898	32.97
1941	43,318	19,176	29,076	18,563	22,321	28,963	96.8	20,417	304,248	38.1	.994	37.91
1942	52,012	20,864	32,317	19,275	23,496	30,030	98.1	20,615	335,866	38.8	1.086	42.17
1943	51,649	19,478	29,046	19,028	23,660	30,540	97.8	20,148	340,498	42.2	1.159	48.94
1944	49,842	19,208	30,709	20,503	23,445	30,815	94.7	21,052	314,888	44.2	1.257	55.53
1945	47,655	19,030	27,622	18,341	19,648	26,479	82.0	18,410	279,274	42.0	1.287	54.03
1946	37,972	20,874	24,463	15,242	15,853	21,287	72.9	15,182	266,835	35.0	1.426	49.91
1947	47,434	24,827	29,639	20,806	21,511	28,570	96.7	20,242	286,316	38.5	1.550	59.64
1948	48,926	26,870	26,795	21,237	22,228	29,292	93.8	20,655	296,785	38.2	1.680	64.21
1949	41,543	23,746	19,181	17,688	19,546	25,807	82.5	18,212	291,163	34.3	1.775	60.94
1950	46,334	26,985	22,280	20,078	23,574	31,457	98.2	22,635	288,265	37.8	1.828	69.10

Production data, which are grouped in broad product classifications, include all production of the materials by the operating subsidiaries and exclude all materials purchased. The average weekly hours and average weekly earnings shown are based on the average monthly number of employees receiving pay. Prior to 1929, the full time equivalent rather than the actual number of employees is shown and, for those early years, the average weekly hours, hourly and weekly earnings have been partially estimated.

*First Calendar Year of Operations

Dollars in millions

Year of oper.	Products & services sold	Employ-ment costs	Products & services bought	Wear and exhaustion	Interest & other costs on debt	Income & other taxes	Income or loss	Preferred stock dividend	Common stock dividend	Reinvested in the business	% Income of sales
1902*	423.1	120.5	160.8	27.8	21.3	2.4	90.3	35.7	20.3	34.3	21.3
1903	398.2	120.8	164.1	29.3	25.6	3.0	55.4	30.4	12.7	12.3	13.9
1904	324.9	101.0	142.3	18.2	30.1	3.1	30.2	25.2	...	5.0	9.3
1905	409.2	128.1	151.1	28.0	29.8	3.6	68.6	25.2	...	43.4	16.8
1906	484.0	147.8	168.7	35.6	29.4	4.4	98.1	25.2	10.2	62.7	20.3
1907	504.4	160.8	169.1	35.1	29.4	5.4	104.6	25.2	10.2	69.2	20.7
1908	331.6	120.5	104.9	23.8	31.3	5.4	45.7	25.2	10.2	10.3	13.8
1909	441.1	151.7	138.4	31.8	31.5	8.7	79.0	25.2	20.3	33.5	17.9
1910	491.8	175.0	157.1	32.5	30.6	9.2	87.4	25.2	25.4	36.8	17.8
1911	431.7	161.6	146.3	27.8	31.1	9.6	55.3	25.2	25.4	4.7	12.8
1912	533.9	189.6	214.3	33.4	32.6	9.8	54.2	25.2	25.4	3.6	10.2
1913	560.8	207.5	191.6	34.0	33.3	13.2	81.2	25.2	25.4	30.6	14.5
1914	412.2	162.7	153.7	26.6	33.2	12.6	23.4	25.2	15.2	17.0d	5.7
1915	523.7	177.3	189.8	34.3	32.8	13.6	75.9	25.2	6.4	44.3	14.5
1916	902.3	263.9	265.3	43.0	32.0	26.6	271.5	25.2	44.5	201.8	30.1
1917	1,284.6	347.9	345.9	83.3	31.0	252.3	224.2	25.2	91.5	107.5	17.5
1918	1,344.6	453.0	339.2	98.8	30.7	297.6	125.3	25.2	71.2	28.9	9.3
1919	1,122.6	479.7	364.5	89.9	30.1	81.6	76.8	25.2	25.4	26.2	6.8
1920	1,290.6	581.8	413.6	80.0	29.3	76.2	109.7	25.2	25.4	59.1	8.5
1921	726.0	333.2	249.9	40.1	28.5	37.7	36.6	25.2	25.4	14.0d	5.0
1922	809.0	323.4	334.7	47.1	28.4	35.8	39.6	25.2	25.4	11.0d	4.9
1923	1,096.5	470.4	377.4	56.9	28.0	55.1	108.7	25.2	29.2	54.3	9.9
1924	921.4	443.6	266.9	53.2	27.3	45.3	85.1	25.2	35.6	24.3	9.2
1925	1,022.0	458.2	333.6	61.6	27.1	50.9	90.6	25.2	35.6	29.8	8.9
1926	1,082.3	469.3	346.7	70.4	26.8	52.4	116.7	25.2	35.6	55.9	10.8
1927	960.5	412.7	323.1	64.4	26.1	46.3	87.9	25.2	49.8	12.9	9.2
1928	1,005.3	402.9	338.4	73.2	25.7	51.0	114.1	25.2	49.8	39.1	11.4
1929	1,097.4	410.2	350.0	69.8	14.9	55.0	197.5	25.2	63.8	108.5	18.0
1930	828.4	371.7	234.8	63.8	5.6	48.1	104.4	25.2	60.4	18.8	12.6
1931	548.7	258.4	187.2	50.4	5.5	34.2	13.0	25.2	37.0	49.2d	2.4
1932	287.7	138.5	141.8	41.6	5.3	31.7	71.2d	20.7	...	91.9d	24.7d
1933	375.0	167.9	161.4	45.3	5.2	31.7	36.5d	7.2	...	43.7d	9.7d
1934	420.9	214.8	140.5	46.4	5.1	35.8	21.7d	7.2	...	28.9d	5.1d
1935	539.4	253.9	191.2	49.8	5.0	38.4	1.1	7.2	...	6.1d	.2
1936	790.5	339.0	287.5	59.0	4.9	49.6	50.5	50.4	...	.1	6.4
1937	1,028.4	447.1	342.6	64.1	5.1	74.6	94.9	58.5	8.7	27.7	9.2
1938	611.1	294.4	228.3	50.3	8.3	37.5	7.7d	25.2	...	32.9d	1.3d
1939	846.0	386.5	293.5	63.4	9.3	52.2	41.1	25.2	...	15.9	4.9
1940	1,079.1	464.3	358.3	72.6	13.6	68.1	102.2	25.2	34.8	42.2	9.5
1941	1,622.3	628.3	604.6	98.6	6.0	168.6	116.2	25.2	34.8	56.2	7.2
1942	1,863.0	782.7	673.4	128.2	6.2	201.3	71.2	25.2	34.8	11.2	3.8
1943	1,972.3	912.9	730.6	134.0	6.3	125.9	62.6	25.2	34.8	2.6	3.2
1944	2,082.2	957.2	814.4	139.0	5.0	105.8	60.8	25.2	34.8	.8	2.9
1945	1,747.3	825.5	670.1	123.4	3.5	66.8	58.0	25.2	34.8	2.0d	3.3
1946	1,496.1	704.5	560.4	68.7	4.8	69.1	88.6	25.2	34.8	28.6	5.9
1947	2,122.8	903.6	839.4	114.0	2.5	136.2	127.1	25.2	45.7	56.2	6.0
1948	2,481.5	1,035.7	1,008.9	146.0	2.4	158.9	129.6	25.2	52.2	52.2	5.2
1949	2,301.7	945.9	885.7	119.7	2.3	182.2	165.9	25.2	56.1	84.6	7.2
1950	2,956.4	1,179.4	1,118.8	143.9	2.2	296.6	215.5	25.2	92.7	97.6	7.3

The data are in some respects necessarily approximate, and are based on the yearly earnings reported annually to stockholders without adjustment for surplus charges and credits except that the years 1942 and 1943 reflect renegotiation settlements made in the succeeding years. For example, taxes are as accrued before adjustments. Employment costs include pensions and social security taxes and, beginning with 1949, also include payments for insurance and other employee benefits. d denotes **deficit**.

*First Calendar Year of Operations

INDEX

f. — the page following
ff. — the pages following

226

FIFTY YEARS OF SERVICE TO THE NATION

USS

1901-1951